To Julie

With blessings of Love and Peace,

Sister Jean

Deprived of Dignity

Children of The Streets and Life After Welfare

Sister Jean Thuerauf

DEPRIVED OF DIGNITY
An Angel Press Book/1997

Cover art: "Comfort" by Steven Olson
Interior design by Betty M. Johnson

Published by
Angel Press
1511 Morgan Avenue North, Minneapolis, MN 55411-3013

ISBN 0-938577-16-6

PRINTED IN THE UNITED STATES OF AMERICA
First Edition.
0987654321

Dedication

To all our generous friends
who have supported
The Mercy Missionaries
throughout the years.

Contents

PART II

PART III

Introduction

When I first came to live in the inner city and establish an outreach Mission House, I had no idea how different life would be. Having lived much of my life in rural settings with white people, I had much to learn. Now, after twenty years as a Mercy Missionary living with so many diverse people of many cultures and creeds, I feel I'm better able to share the inside story.

Living on the inside of the inner city for so long a time gives me a unique perspective that I wouldn't have had otherwise. Not only did I have an opportunity to meet people on their turf, I also was able to develop personal relationships with them. It's from these relationships I learned the how and the why of what I was experiencing.

Another great advantage was living in the same area for twenty years. Over this span of time, I followed the comings and goings of families and learned the reasons for their movements. Also, it has been interesting to follow individuals of these families and learn the why behind their behavior.

In our society today, we're making monumental decisions affecting all of us. We need to share our visions and dreams, express our fears and hopes, and creatively plan and implement our ideas.

It's important all of us be informed of the true inner city story, whether we're serving on the Social Awareness Committee of our local church, or as politicians representing a certain area. The true story of the inner city is precisely the purpose of this book, together with the sharing of suggestions and ideas for future discussion.

Sister Jean Thuerauf

Acknowledgements

Sincere thanks to the Loretto Sisters of Nerinx, Kentucky and the Immaculate Heart Sisters of Tucson, Arizona for providing retreat havens in which to compile the thoughts for this book.Our thanks, too, to all the people who contributed their talents to help make this book possible.

PART I

Chapter 1

Tragedy of the Inner City Poor

Before we launch into a description of the urban plight in our inner cities, I'll define who I mean by the poor. Poor people are often those who can't hold up their heads. They sometimes mumble rather than talk, address you with downcast eyes, or have pockets with holes in them. Poor people can also be described as those who often sleep during the day and prowl streets and alleys at night. Such people have laid claim to the night, believing that in darkness a certain freedom can be enjoyed not found in the daytime.

Too often over the past years I've seen both young and grown children trudge slowly down the middle of the street. They carry heavy sticks and table legs, their heads hanging low. When they approach our Mission House, they ring the doorbell impatiently, then sit quietly, awaiting some longed-for attention. Their sad faces brighten as I greet them and ask what they'd like. In unison, their reply is, "Nothin!" They know I don't like them to beg; therefore, they try to avoid offending me. When I tell them I'll get them a surprise, they come alive, chattering among themselves, anticipating their surprise with excitement.

Children who come to the Mission House are hungry for food, but more important, they crave attention and affection. Like the other neighborhood children and the desperate families and non-families they represent, they're the poor of our inner city. They're the foremost subjects of our concern.

Randy's Desperation

Randy and his little brothers came to our Mission House often during their early growing-up days. They were much in need of someone to care for them. They lived with their alcoholic mother in an upstairs hovel. Often the boys would search our backyard dumpster for something to eat.

Crack-House Tara

Tara lived in a crack house. When her turn came to be my "handy helper," she was delighted. Tara and I were busy baking a cake when she asked if I had a drink of water. I poured her some cold water from the pitcher in the refrigerator. Soon Tosha came to join us.

"Guess what, Tosha! Sister Jean knows how to make cold water!" exclaimed Tara.

Later, I discovered there was no refrigerator in Tara's house. It had been sold to buy cocaine.

Naked in the Park

As I walked through the park one bright summer morning, I noticed a strange movement in the tall grass. I drew nearer and was astounded to see two small naked children lying on top of each other. Their clothes were in a heap nearby. Evidently, they'd run away from their sick Grandma and decided to play in the park. Close by were the new swings and merry-

go-round the Park Board had just installed. The boys didn't even know how to play!

Sleepless Kesha

Kesha ran to catch up with me. As she walked beside me, I noticed her eyes were almost shut. I asked her if she was tired.

"Yes, I am!" she quickly responded.

"Didn't you go to bed last night?" I inquired.

"Not until the sun was comin' up," sleepy Kesha told me as she laid her head against me."

Lack of Curiosity

Children such as those I've described lack enthusiasm. They're not ready to go into the big beautiful world, see and hear different things, or venture into the unknown. No, children raised in unhealthy environments, trapped by fears of addicted adults, soon lose their curiosity. Their world is a darkened room with TV blaring soap operas and adults yelling obscenities.

Lack of Imagination

Along with a lack of curiosity, there's the inability to imagine. Their sense of awe and wonder haven't been given an opportunity to develop. Consequently, these inner city poor children are incapable of dreaming. With their creative abilities limited, they can't fulfill the expectations of their teachers.

Lack of Purpose

Children who haven't been allowed to develop creative abilities at an early age become frustrated, saddened, and begin hating themselves. Without dreams, they lack purpose in their lives and turn to all kinds of dangerous and negative behaviors to alleviate frustration.

Ballet Tommy

When Tommy was in sixth grade, he captured everyone's attention with his ballet talent. He was always happy to show his dancing steps to whomever would watch, peers or adults. When Tommy was offered a scholarship to a New York Dancing School, I shared in the joy of the moment. But a short time later, I was saddened to learn that when Tommy went to the airport, he was too frightened to get on the plane and returned to his street friends.

Nicky Told a Lie

The ring toss game was over. I was picking up leftover prizes and asked, "Does anyone have a birthday in July?"

There was a moment of silence; a few children responded with negative nods. Then in a whispered voice, Nicky said, "I had one on July 4th."

I noticed dubious looks on the other children, but we went ahead and celebrated. There was a special card, gift, and piece of gum for all. Later, as I was leaving, I noticed two boys walk off with Nicky, seemingly telling him something of importance. I waited.

Nicky came over to me with his head hanging. "I told a lie." he whispered, as he handed me his gift and card.

I told him I was happy he had the courage to be honest.

He said, "Those guys helped me."

Then I reached into my bag and pulled out three tennis balls, one for each.

"I Want the Mommy!"

When the kids came at their appointed time to write their Pen Pals, I noticed a stranger among them. "She's our cousin," they told me.

After telling her I'd look up the name of a girl her age, she said, "No, I want the Mommy!"

Homeless Jason

I was ready to lock the door when I heard a sad voice, "They're taking me away from my Dad; I don't know what to do."

I invited the frail little eight-year old in to tell me his troubles. He poured out his story about how his Mom was drinking and wanted him to come live with her so she could get more money.

Jason interrupted his story with sobs and cried, "I just wish my Mom was dead!"

He put his head in his dirty arms and cried, "I don't even know where they're going to send my brothers, either."

I took the little boy in my arms and asked the Lord to help him stay with his Dad. Later, he came by to tell me they had changed their minds and he could stay. I knew my prayer was answered.

Gang Development

Lacking the structure of a secure home life, the poor of our cities are undisciplined for the most part. They look at anyone in authority as threats to their existence. These children begin grouping together at a very early age, always looking to the older and larger for leadership and advice.

Once in a group, their hands come out of their pockets and are used to carry weapons, chains, clubs, table legs, or even steel fence posts. In a group they feel a sense of power and set out conquering whomever or whatever fits their need of the moment. If they're hungry, they'll steal food; if they're bored, they'll vandalize property. Children in a group easily fall prey to destructive behavior they wouldn't think of doing as individuals. Children don't learn responsibility unless they're living in an environment where they have appropriate role models. If they're not treated with respect, they won't respect those who attempt to discipline them. They'll rebel and react negatively, rather than conform and adjust favorably.

We might well look at early behaviors as a root cause of violence among youth today.

Need for Chains

The kid from Chicago was just visiting. As usual, he was equipped with defense weapons. I explained that the chains he had crudely nailed to a wooden handle had to be left on the porch before he could accompany his friends into my house as guests, so he hid his chains under the bench and came in. Later, after a quiet tour filled with stories of love and wonder, and a prayerful party of punch and apple pie, the boys were leaving and awkwardly thanked me for everything. Then one of them picked up the chains and handed them to the Chicago kid.

I asked, "Do you think you really need those?"

"Sister Jean, he has to have 'em cause he has to go back tomorrow, and he don't have any chance to learn about God," one of the lads explained.

Bike Problems

When a generous friend gifted me with a bike, I realized the challenge was to give it away peacefully. I decided to put in a box the names of all the children who lived in one geographical area, then have a drawing. After a prayer, a name was drawn, and the winner matched the size of the bike perfectly. The only problem was that Stephanie didn't know how to ride a bike, but her brothers, sisters, and cousins offered to help her learn. Then I noticed angry and jealous looks on the loser's faces. They were ready to spring into revenge. Words didn't seem to help, and I wondered how these children could be taught instantly about peace, respect, and self-control. Several days later, a teary-eyed brother related the tragedy of his sister's bike.

"These kids just came and stole it and ripped off the wheels," he sadly told me.

Shivering Montague

Late one chilly evening the doorbell rang. I wondered who it could be shivering in the cold at that hour. I pulled the door open and there stood my friend, Montague.

"I come to talk to you," blurted the half-frozen 15-year old.

Once inside, sipping hot chocolate and eating sandwiches, Montague acted as though he'd be staying all night. He said no one wanted him. He had stayed his time at the shelter. There was no foster home for him, and his name was on a long list at a group home. He added that he couldn't stand it in his own home.

Then I remembered a game I'd received, and I gave it to Montague. He was thrilled and with a warm scarf, cap, mittens, a sack of cookies, and a prayer, I sent him on his way. As I watched him go out into the cold darkness, I wondered about the reality of love today and whether there was something more I should do?

Several days later, Montague excitedly told me, "Guess what! My Mom is going to use that game against me. She said I stole it."

When I told him to have her call me, he said, "Oh no, I can get into the Group Home faster if she says I stole it!"

Red Jacketed Boy

Kicking rocks into the air was one way to tell the world he was angry. I guessed the boy in the red jacket must have had a run-in with someone. My imagination played with what could have happened. Suddenly my musings were interrupted with a cracking, tree-breaking sound. I turned quickly and there it was: a fallen two-year old tree and a scared, red-jacketed boy heading west.

Yearning To Belong

Probably the most heart-rending and saddest element of being poor in our inner city is the feeling of not belonging. Where there's no stable family unit, children are left to find their own security. Since this is impossible for the very young, they're left with devastating effects.

Children want people to like them. They're very sensitive as to how others, especially adults, regard them. Sometimes when they're ashamed of the way their parents conduct themselves, they'll try covering for them with lies and make-believe stories. Some children make up new last names so they aren't associated with guilty parents.

If children are surrounded by people with dysfunctional behavior and have no positive role models, they can't relate to what a real family is. Consequently, the cycle is continued. Only the violence and erratic behavior worsens as it's exemplified in each subsequent generation.

Little Fellow Waiting

The tiny lad sat on the bakery steps. His hair was matted, face smeared with dirt, and toes poked through his tennis shoes.

The little fellow sat and waited because his brother mysteriously died, his mother went away, and his father was in jail.

'Cream Truck

The little boys, two and three years old, stood on the curb. I heard one say, "that not it," as a big moving van whizzed by. Then again I heard, "that not it," as a mail truck swished by.

I stopped and asked, "What are you looking for?"

"We want 'cream truck," replied one of the little fellows as he showed me a crumpled food stamp.

I could feel their hunger, and I knew these boys were among the many uncared for children who are victims of "cracked" parents.

Substitute Mother

It was Friday before Mother's Day. The assignment in Art was to make something for Mother.

Tim stopped at my door on his roundabout way home and said, "Here, you can have this, I gots the meanest Mom in the whole world."

My arms and heart went out to him standing there so alone and forlorn. As I put his big black butterfly in my window, I realized what it meant to be "Mother."

Farewell Kids

Two of my little friends, ages five and seven, stood at the door. "We're going away tonight after dark," they stammered.

"Oh, are you coming back?" I asked.

"Nope, Mom says we're going away forever and we won't see you again," they answered sadly.

Later, as I thought about my farewell kids, hot tears trickled down my cheeks. I hadn't had time to teach the whole story of God's love.

Little did I know that later that day they would reappear and announce, "We didn't go because we couldn't find anyone to take us."

Life in Crack Houses

The world of the drug addict is a dangerous and inhuman world. No child should have to live there. One begins to wonder how to do charity in such surroundings. Passing out food and clothes is so temporary. Clothes won't be washed when they become dirty; they'll be thrown away. Furniture will be sold for more drugs. Money will be used to feed the habit while conditions worsen.

There's nothing normal about life in a "crack house." There are no meals around a family table. Even animals eating around a common trough seem to fend better than some children in crack-infested homes.

Dirty clothes and garbage are everywhere. Cockroaches and rats abound. The air is filled with foul odors.

Though landlords put on storm windows to bring houses up to code, inside windows aren't lowered to keep out winter's chill. Bags of garbage don't seem to make it to disposal bins, becoming strewn about hallways and yards by dogs, cats, and squirrels.

Noise is another devastating influence in crack houses. Because TV and radio are constantly blaring, people can't talk in low voices. They must yell at each other. Competition among young children to be heard rivals any hog-calling contest.

Because money is needed for drugs, renters invite other relatives and friends to share their small space, and children get squeezed together into small spaces.

Children are unable to claim any shelves in a cupboard or drawers in a dresser. They soon become discouraged trying to hang on to something of their own. Without their own teddy bears, mittens, or even shoes, they lose their last bit of personal security and become discouraged.

Children living in an atmosphere of constant violence, sirens blaring, and people yelling, soon learn it does them no good to cry for help. They silently cry their pain of neglect into their inner selves.

Jason's Lost Mother

"They don't know where my Mom is. They think she's dead," Jason informed me.

Jason lives in a crack house. He and his brother seemed to be deposited there for the time being. The two brothers were pale, white, and skinny. They were strangers to the other ten black kids who lived with them. I'm not sure if Jason was more scared than hungry, or more lonesome than scared or hungry, but I know he was crying when he came over to me and sobbed, "I hope I can go to the same school as last year so I'll at least know somebody."

Run Away Joseph

The house had been raided and was now condemned. Trash was strewn about the front and back yards. Windows were broken. It was the night before their moving day. I was startled by the doorbell. "Who could want something at this late hour?" I wondered as I flipped on the light and peered out. I could see no one. When I opened the door, there was three-year-old, barefoot Joseph. Big tears were streaming down his cheeks.

"I wanna stay with you!" he cried. "I don't wanna go with them!"

Bus Missing Jamie

It was a beautiful October afternoon. Jamie ran to tell me he couldn't go to school. He explained his Mom had a party and it was too noisy to sleep, so he couldn't get to sleep until the party was over, and didn't wake up in time for the bus.

Too Many Teenage Mothers

Young girls living in a hostile, aggressive environment soon learn how to protect themselves. They have babies and more babies to insure a sense of personal security. When this behavior is encouraged by additional welfare subsidies, it seems so right for the young and immature.

It's sad to see young, pregnant teenage girls select coloring books as their birthday gifts. Something was missing, and they failed to grow into maturity. Boys and girls who don't have their emotional needs met in their early teens, make undesirable choices that have devastating effects on their later lives.

Without positive role models, young teens can't help but repeat the behaviors of their elders. To them, producing a baby is a real sign of maturity.

Grandma Sandra and Her 48 Babies

Sandra pulled the door open and asked me to come in. I had to look before I sat down, because the room was dark and babies were everywhere. There were forty-eight babies in baskets, on the couch and floor, and crawling all over me. Sandra babysits each night while her seven young daughters go out on the streets to earn a living in the only way they know how.

Shanda and Her Baby

Thirteen-year old Shanda brought her new baby girl to show me. She was wet with sweat. The month was July and the day was hot. The baby had on two sweaters! Shanda ignored my counsel to put something cooler on her baby as she blurted, "We're hoping my stepsister's baby will be a boy. That way, we won't have to worry about the HIV virus."

"You Bring Us Some Candy?"

Two very young girls with babies moved in down the street. I decided to pay a visit to my new neighbors. Climbing the steps to their apartment, I prayed for patience. Since the doorbell was broken, I rapped. There was much noise within. I banged. Someone yelled, "Who is it?"

I yelled my name back. Then I heard them move some furniture. At last, the door opened a bit. Now I could see the inhuman mess: five teenagers and four babies all yelling at each other.

One of the young mothers shouted, "You bring us some candy?"

Chaquatta's Diarrhea Cure

Eight-year old Chaquatta quickened her steps as she pushed the baby carriage toward me. It was then I noticed something strange. The baby had his legs sticking straight up and his poor little head was down at the foot of the carriage.

When I asked why, Chaquatta said simply, "He has diarrhea, and I didn't want it to come out."

Samuel The Baby Maker

"How many babies do you have by now?" I asked the young boy on the phone. Samuel proudly said, "Five, and two more on the way."

Astounded and angry, I said, "I don't want to see you! I talked to you before about doing things in the right order, and if you don't change your behavior, I don't want to see you again."

Then I hung up.

The next day, Samuel called and said, "I changed my behavior."

I invited him to come over. We prayed and ate and talked once more about responsibility. As he went out the door to look for a job, I wondered about the many things he told me:

(1) The seven babies have seven different mothers and none want Samuel;
(2) All are taken care of by the government;
(3) The girls made deals with Samuel to get them pregnant;
(4) Samuel is hungry now because he has no more girl friends;
(5) Samuel felt safe in not accepting responsibility because he has no job.

Addiction Subtracts Consciences

Drug addicts lose the delicate sensibility of their consciences. They lack direction, like ships without rudders, seeking nothing worthwhile. Their world becomes a barren and forbidden wilderness. With stony faces harboring blurred, bloodshot eyes, and arms displaying gang symbols and scars of self-mutilation, they ignore friendly greetings. These people no longer dream nor can they believe in academic pursuits. Their world becomes one of despair. They care little about police records.

In fact, one wonders whether these people regard our overly humane prisons and treatment centers to be respite places from the jungle of the streets.

Lasting Lessons of Love

Two members of the Vice Lord Street Gang sat on the porch bench and waited for my return.

"You guys know I can't invite you into my house if you have weapons," I told them.

"Yup, we knew we were comin' here, so we left them behind."

"Well, I guess I'll just have to trust you," I said as I opened the door for them.

One of them put out his hand and showed me a festering sore. "Do you have a band-aid? I remember when I sat over there and licked the frosting pan and you took my picture."

After I treated his sore, I brought out the scrapbooks. For the next half hour, I learned the whereabouts of many "old" friends. Such an experience can be both discouraging and exhilarating. Yes, it's sad to learn so many of our young kids join street gangs, but, at the same time, it's encouraging to know that lessons of love experienced in early years are everlasting.

Ray The Gang Kid

Eight-year old Ray, dressed in his gang colors, sat on his porch and asked, "Can I come in your yard?"

"No, Ray, I can't let you. You should be in school, and I don't want gang kids in my yard," I answered.

Ray disappeared inside and came out dressed in his regulars.

I asked him, "Why aren't you in school?"

"I ain't in school 'cause they suspended me for startin' a fight," Ray proudly told me.

That evening, when I saw his Mom take him by the hand and lead him to the ice cream truck, I knew the case of school vs. boy had been defeated.

Robin's Beating

Robin showed me her back. It was scarred from the heavy chain. She had been riding her bike when a big guy knocked her off and took it from her. When she resisted, he pulled a chain from his pocket and began whipping her.

Amanda's Mother's Murderer

Amanda shouted, "I'm never ever going to that place again."

I asked, "Why not? Isn't that a nice place?"

"The lady that murdered my mother works there. She only got two years in prison. That's not enough; she killed my mother!" sobbed Amanda as she leaned on my shoulder.

Bedless Molique

Molique stood at the door and asked, "Is you alone?"

I told her I was and ushered her into the kitchen. She stammered, "Last night my mom stole my bed. She needed it to shoot up in. She stole my purple sweater, too. Now she's stolen everything I have. I hate my Mom. I don't have anyone who loves me now."

I hugged Molique tightly and wondered who would care for this forlorn twelve-year old.

Chapter II

Moral Devastation

After reading the heart-rendering stories of the first chapter, one can't help conclude there's a devastating disease corroding our nation. It's a disease of the soul destroying the heart of our country. A more powerful balm than money is required to heal this disease.

To understand the nature of this growing epidemic, I've held imaginary interviews with some of my street friends. These conversations give us some insight into the question, "Why?"

Imprisoned Tom

At last, the prison guards finished their questioning, testing, and searching, so I was free to go to Cell Block No. 2 and wait my turn to go to the window. It was a long time since I'd seen Tom. I knew him so well as a little boy, I often wondered what happened in his life that led him to rape ten women, earning him a sentence of 138 years without parole.

I held his picture I brought with me from our Mission scrapbook. Who would've thought such a gentle and loving boy would become such a wild, ferocious, animalistic human?

When Tom came to the window, I tried composing myself and quickly wiped my tears away.

"Tom, what happened?" I decided to be direct as our time together was so limited.

"Sister Jean, remember when I was little and didn't want to talk about my Mom and never wanted to leave you? I hated living with my cousins. My Mom was in jail, and I got mad at everyone. I didn't care what I did or who I hurt. At first I stole, then I started doing drugs, then I raped all those girls. Yes, I was mad! I deserve to be in here. I better stay here because I can't trust myself. Sister Jean, thanks for all the love you gave me. I think about that so much. Will you pray for me?"

I assured him of my love and prayers and told him I'd continue to love him, and I knew Jesus loved him, too!

Of course, I couldn't give him that hug he so needed, but I trust the Lord's peace will be with him as he endures the long torturous years in prison.

This is the little boy, who, when he was but six years old, refused to write his mother's name on the flower-painted tank decorated for that purpose.

When I asked him why, he angrily cried, "She's in jail, she's bad!" Tom was always the last to leave the Mission House. He clung to my apron as if he was afraid to go "home."

The moral development of children is dependent on role models who teach by their words and give witness by their actions. When these models are missing in early childhood, there are inevitably dire consequences later.

Probation Jimmy

I was happy to see Jimmy at my door. We had so much to catch up on since I last saw him. As usual, I started our conversation with, "How long have you been out this time?"

"About two weeks, but they'll soon have me in again. I have a record, you know," responded Jimmy.

"I know, Jimmy, What has happened? Remember when you came to ask me to pray with you because you wanted to get that mowing job?"

"Yes, and I got it, too, but it didn't last, 'cause they put me in for burglary. Tiara and I stole some food from the store," Jimmy explained.

"Jimmy, I can't believe you would rather take the risk of being slammed in jail than ask for help. Didn't your job pay enough?" I asked him.

Jimmy looked at me and confessed, "I was gonna have another baby and I needed more money than that mowin' job could give me. You know, Sister Jean, I really don't want to go wrong. You say the Lord blesses. Well, he ain't blessing me."

I asked Jimmy about his Mom. "Oh, she disowned me when I stole a car. She said I wasn't smart enough to get by with it. You know, she's not my real Mom. She just vanned us up here so she could get more money. Now she says I'm stupid; I don't know how to play the game. Really, Sister Jean, no one cares about me. I might go to Mississippi and see if I can find my real father."

A week later, Larry came to tell me that Jimmy went on a bus to Mississippi. Three weeks later, Jimmy was again at my door.

"Sister Jean, I'm back. My dad's girlfriend threw me out 'cause I ate too much. Do you have another paper sack? I can't return these pants in this one. It got wet in the rain."

I looked at the pants and could see they were dirty. "Are these the ones you wore on the bus?" I asked.

"Those are the ones. Now I need the money worse than the pants, so I'm gonna return them," Jimmy explained.

Lack of Parental Role Models

Again, as in Tom's story, we see the result of lack of parental role models. This is the same lad who called from prison to ask if I'd send the picture of him working that I had in my scrapbook.

He said, "They don't believe I'm any good and that picture will tell them they're wrong."

When children aren't affirmed, they're soon convinced they're worthless and lose motivation to learn and dream.

Knowing that is enough to understand why Jimmy kept making babies. He thought he'd find his worth if one of the "mothers" would accept him and let him live with her and the baby. Jimmy fathered eight children with seven different girls before he was twenty-two years old.

When he showed me the picture of his eighth child, he said, "I thought for sure this time I could be a real father."

After that, Jimmy was devastated and went on to live the life of a drug addict on the streets.

Josh Learns to Loot

Josh came to chat about his family. He told me they went to live with his aunt after his mom died. He remembered there were four kids in a bed.

"We had to lie crosswise so we'd fit," he explained.

He recalled how he, his brothers and cousins would come to the Mission House always expecting a handout. He remembered how he could never help at the Mission because auntie had sent them out to steal.

"We were told to steal bikes, TVs, anything she could strip in the basement and resell. We learned quickly how to mug

people, and there was always a reward when we returned with our loot," Josh explained.

Without hardly a breath, he continued, "Then we joined the Vice Lords. Once in the gang, we didn't come to the Mission House anymore. Our lives were filled with violence and crime. Two of my cousins have been killed; four of them are in jail; some of us are on the run. We want to give it all up but are living scared."

When I learned Josh's aunt and other relatives were fencing in the basement of their home, I knew the reason why all the cousins would gather together and go out to steal whatever they could. Sometimes it was a bike. Other times, they entered homes and carried out all the electronic equipment. Everything would be de-identified in the basement before being resold to the underground market.

Josh's hope is to find a mentor, a friend who'll take him away from his environment before it's too late.

Julia and Her Free Meal Calendar

Julia invited me into her house. She needed to tell me about her family's waywardness. Her kids hadn't gone in the direction she'd hoped. She showed me pictures of two of her boys I knew when they were young. My friends and I tutored them when they were in their elementary grades. Now they both had become "girls" and were gay. She told me her husband committed suicide and one of her sons killed his friend in a fit of anger.

I remembered how this same lady had shown me her calendar, so I could see each day marked with the location of where she could take her family for a free meal. She explained it was easiest that way, because she didn't need as many groceries, or have to teach the kids how to cook and do dishes.

Perhaps someone should have taught Julia the role of mother and wife. Maybe if there'd been a class on parenting instead of trigonometry during her education days, she might have learned how to nurture her children.

Would the tragedies of Julia's life have been prevented if children and parents had come together around a family table for a common meal? Such an experience gives nourishment to both body and soul.

Joe's Chickens

Joe showed me a crate of live chickens he had in his yard. Sometime later, he called me in to receive one of those hens all dressed and frozen.

I believe the need to give is as great as the need to get. After carrying the heavy hen around in my bag for three hours, my need to give was also great!

Impromptu Birthday

"When is your birthday, Sister Jean?" asked the noisy and excited children.

I told them it was long ago one day last September.

They said, "We could celebrate it anyway."

They had a birthday cake they'd just gotten among the "handouts" given away weekly.

Soon I was seated at the table with a bunch of dirty, ragged, hungry, and happy children who wanted to share their goodies with me. As I looked into the eyes of those children, I knew we didn't need any candles. The light that shined from them was enough for us.

26¢ Smile

Recently, a fellow handed me 26¢. He said it was for smiling and waving at him one day last June. He said he'd been feeling really down and was leaning out his apartment window. I came along, waved, and smiled at him, and made his day. He also said when he noticed I was alone and didn't carry a purse, he knew I was for real. He added that he hoped he could help me even more sometime, and I hoped so, too!

Angelita's Gift

Angelita called to me as I went past her home.

"Please come in. I have something special for you."

She scurried to the bedroom and brought out a blue wool dress, two sizes too small.

"I found this dress at the clothes place and thought of you," she told me.

As I carried the blue dress home, I wondered what the world would be like if it was filled with more people like Angelita.

Sarah's Botched Suicide

Sarah had recently attempted suicide. When I called and invited her to lunch, I could hardly hear her tired and depressed response. I fixed a simple lunch and prayed the Lord would send her to me. At last, helped by two children, Sarah swaggered into the kitchen. I ushered her to a chair, and immediately, she seemed to feel at home. She poured out her heart as we ate our sandwiches.

When Sarah was leaving, she said, "Thanks for being my friend; I've told you more than I'd even tell my own sister."

Jeb Hates Prison

"I can't go back, Sister Jean. I hate that prison. They don't let you do anything, and they watch you all the time." The words tumbled nonstop from my 18-year old friend, Jeb.

"Are you running again?" I asked him, wondering why he came.

"No, I just feel like it," Jeb replied. "They let me out on a pass for the weekend. I sure don't feel like going back."

For a long time Jeb and I talked. He recalled the time he helped me bake cookies and wondered if I still had his picture. He told me he had sent $5.00 to his Mom to help her out. When I reached over and took his hand to tell him I always believed he was good and loving way down inside, his face shown with hope and he smiled his question. "If I go back and finish my prison time, can I come and work in your bakery?"

I answered, "Yes, Jeb," and wondered how and when that miracle would happen.

Scropia, The Moth

Last summer when I found a huge Scropia moth, I didn't realize how valuable such a nature treasure could become. Frequently, Muffles, the moth, would come with me when I went out to meet people.

One day I came upon a gang of teenage boys. "Hey, you guys, I have something in this box you've never seen before," I called to them from across the street. They looked at each other and began approaching me. I gave the leader the box.

He lifted the lid and exclaimed, "Wow! Is that for real? Where'd you get it?"

The questions were many, and I quickly gave some details of the fascinating creature. Without a doubt, I knew the thoughts of those six boys were, at least for a brief time, thoughts of reverence and awe. I also know these are the same boys that wave and greet me as I stroll through the park.

The Horror of Life Without Love

I believe all people were created and redeemed out of Love. Consequently, love is within each human person. Yes, buried in the heart of each is a tiny seed of God's love, life, and goodness. With proper nourishment and environment, it will grow and bloom. Without nourishment, it will die.

Sometimes, it takes keen eyesight and fine-tuned hearing to sense goodness when it's revealed to us.

It's only when we believe in the goodness of others that mutual sharing can happen. Then, and only then, is trust established, and are relationships formed. Through these relationships, seeds of goodness are nourished and their flowers bloom.

When we take a close look at our world, we see a sinful, perverse, unloving place filled with people who have become paralyzed with passion and evil. On TV and billboards, advertisements are everywhere, bombarding us with the thought that having more means "The Good Life." Sometimes people tend to stand firm, get a solid grip on what they possess, then withdraw into themselves by either carrying weapons or making fists to guard against attack, fearing they'll become destitute and threadbare if they don't.

When we witness the rampant destruction of life and see the raw wounds of humanity, we're tempted to find a rapid solution. It's so easy to adopt a problem-solving attitude toward life and believe that any difficulty, regardless of its complexity, can be ultimately surmounted with sufficient money and brainpower.

Ours is a violent society. Anyone living in our inner cities is well aware of the godlessness of that environment. Without a sense of the sacredness of life, people react against rather than respond to each other, behaving impulsively and violently when their desires aren't met. In short, the quality of life soon shrivels to the lowest grade of living, which is a subhuman, animalistic existence. How can there be any awareness of God's love if life itself becomes cheap and worthless?

Shalanda's story, ***Out of the Darkness***, is about real people living in our city. Her story gives us hope, that what once seemed impossible is truly possible with God's help.

Chapter III

Out of the Darkness

Shalanda turned over and relished the fact she could sleep until noon. Having been on the streets until 5:00 a.m., her body felt tired, not at all ready for another day. She was glad the East window was covered with a bedspread so the sun couldn't shine in. Shalanda was glad, too, that her mother was staying with her and would care for the baby a couple of days. The other two kids would get breakfast at school.

"Anybody home?" someone was shouting at the front door.

"Who's there?" Shalanda drowsily asked as she pulled aside the spread.

"I've been sent from Housing. You called about the roaches?" asked the uniformed man with a nozzle spray.

"Yes, about a week ago," Shalanda told him.

"Lady, you should have everything out of your cupboards. I'll be back tomorrow."

He slammed the door and Shalanda stumbled back to bed.

The clock struck noon. Shalanda rushed out to get the mail. She didn't want to miss her last check. She couldn't think about what she'd do after that.

Just then, Ray came to sit and wait on the top step of her porch. After Shalanda cashed her check, he'd get his portion. After all, he was the baby's father and had made a deal when she wanted him to make her pregnant. Now it was time to get paid.

Just then, Johnnie came stomping into the kitchen. Shalanda wished he could stay in school all day, but they brought him home at 11:30. She gave him some dry cereal for his lunch.

"Can I play outside?" he asked, anxious to play in the new snow.

After Shalanda nodded her consent, Johnnie hurriedly put on his jacket, took the lid off the garbage can, and slid down the well-worn hill in front of his house.

Just then, the mailman came. Shalanda grabbed the check and told Johnnie he had to come with her. Grandma would have enough to do looking after Timmy and the baby.

They headed to the bank. This was going to be a big day. First, the wait in line at the bank. Johnnie always hated that; he'd rather have played with his garbage lid in the snow. After a long time, they trudged back home to pay Ray. He needed to be paid before all the money was spent.

The next wait was at the bus stop. So many people were heading for the supermarket, the bus was very crowded. Johnnie knew he'd have to stand all the way to the store, but he also knew he wouldn't fall, since he was securely pressed between an old man with a stick and his mom.

Shalanda remembered the Housing Office closed at 3:00 p.m.. She buzzed the bus to stop. At last, Johnnie could breathe again. The cold air felt good. He put one hand in his sleeve and clung to his mom's hand with the other.

Slowly they made their way through the crowd at Housing to the window with a sign that read, "Rent Paid Here." Shalanda took a number, and since there were no seats left, she leaned against the wall and waited for her number 48 to be called. Just then, she heard 28 and knew it would be a long wait. Johnnie clung to his mom's leg and wished again he was sliding on that garbage lid.

One hour and 28 minutes later, Shalanda heard 48 called. She breathed a sigh of relief and woke sleeping Johnnie who had collapsed at her feet.

"Let's see, Shalanda Mallow, is that right?" asked the clerk shuffling some cards and turning to her computer. "It says here you owe $350 for a double bedroom in the Fillmore Projects."

"Oh, last month it was $325. Why is it more?" asked Shalanda wondering what she would have after the bills were paid.

"I know. The government said everyone had to sacrifice," the clerk responded calmly as she recounted the cash Shalanda handed her.

Shalanda walked out, dragging Johnnie behind her. The boy was so tired and hungry he could hardly walk. She told him he could have an ice cream cone when they got to the store.

Shalanda was relieved to find the gas and electric office down the hall still open and the line short. But when the clerk said her bill was $140, she had a sick feeling in the pit of her stomach. Shalanda was hoping there'd be enough left for food so she wouldn't have to go to the streets that night. Then she thought of the pampers Grandma needed for the baby and the birthday present for Timmy.

With her dwindling cash, she headed to the food stamp window. She tucked a $20 bill in her bra knowing it would be secure there and no one, no, not anyone would find it!

Having purchased the stamps, she headed out the door and down the street to the bus stop. A loaded bus was just pulling out, so she and little Johnnie leaned against the building and waited for another. It was then Shalanda realized how very tired she was. She looked down at Johnnie. He lay fast asleep on the sidewalk. Shalanda thought about her mom at home with the baby and Tim. She wished she was there to help ease their hunger. Suddenly, a bus screeched to a stop and Shalanda was awakened from her musings. She pulled Johnnie to his feet and they quickly got on.

Again coins jingled in the box and Shalanda wondered how many she'd have left for her return trip. The bus was crowded, so they both had to stand. At last, it stopped near the supermarket and Shalanda and Johnnie were once again in the cool air, except now the sun was gone and darkness had already set in.

Johnnie remembered the cone and pleaded, "Mom, you said when we got to the store...."

Shalanda shuffled to the counter and ordered a cone. She was mighty happy to have a chance to sit down as Johnnie hungrily ate his cone. While Johnnie ate, Shalanda counted the food stamps and cash she had left. She knew she needed to save one book of stamps for later, so she planned to spend one, plus the $10 in cash. She hoped it would buy toilet paper, dish soap, and Pampers.

Johnnie's energy revived for a bit; he wanted to push the cart. Shalanda went down the dairy product aisle. She pulled milk, margarine, and eggs off the shelves, then moved on to fresh fruits and vegetables. She was happy to see the mustard greens her mother liked so much.

By now Johnnie was dragging behind, too tired to push or keep up with the cart. Shalanda told him to sit under the basket and ride. Then she bought pork hocks, corn meal, and bread, and headed to the checkout. The cashier quickly rang up the bill and asked for $38.34. Shalanda knew that would take some of the stamps from her second book.

After packing six bags, Shalanda looked around for Johnnie. He had ventured over to pull levers on a video machine, so she looked at a group of men huddled in the corner. Then she asked one she recognized if he'd take them home.

Elmer was glad to oblige. He looked forward to the $3.00 he'd be paid for the trip, and Shalanda was glad to get home. Elmer helped her with the bags, and Shalanda thanked him, and gave him $3.00.

Shalanda found the milk, poured some in a nursing bottle and gave it to her fussing baby. Grandma was happy to see the mustard greens and pork hocks. She immediately set about boiling some for their dinner.

Tim came running to see if there was anything like a birthday present in the bags.

"Tim, I didn't get it yet, but tomorrow I'll be able to."

He looked disappointed and went to see if Johnnie wanted to play. He found him fast asleep on the couch.

After dinner, Shalanda sat on the end of the couch holding her baby Rosalee. Grandma was busy cleaning up the kitchen. Already it was 8 o'clock and bedtime for the children. Shalanda was too tired and grandma was too busy, so the boys slipped into bed without brushing their teeth or taking a bath. They were soon both asleep dreaming of good times in the snow with garbage lids. The baby was content and fast asleep in her crib, and grandma had gone to her room. Shalanda was ready to call it a day when a loud rap came on the door.

It was some old friends who came to see if Shalanda wanted to "live it up." They had a bottle. Shalanda was ready for some fun. She had a hard day and a little drink would be relaxing.

It wasn't long before the foursome were laughing and shouting, unaware that a grandma, baby, and two small boys were trying to sleep. So were the upstairs neighbors. Eventually, one of the drunken men opened his crack bag, emptied it into a bottle and handed it to Shalanda. Almost immediately she sensed a "high" and wanted more. Soon all were crazed with drugs and alcohol and stumbled out into the street. There they sprawled in the yard, rolling on top of each other, half-dazed until Shalanda finally groped her way back into the house and flopped on the couch.

The next morning, grandma awoke to hear the baby crying, and the boys were chasing each other around the kitchen table. Her back ached with arthritis and her head was pounding. "Wake up, Shalanda, it's time you took care of this family.

Johnnie just missed his bus and now he won't get any breakfast," yelled grandma.

Shalanda rolled off the couch and stumbled over to the corner to pick up the screaming baby. She put some milk in the bottle and rocked the baby back to sleep. Shalanda went to see if she could find some clean clothes for Tim. Finally, she turned a dirty shirt inside out and found some oversized pants in a bag in a corner of the room.

"Here, wear these today 'till I get some washed," she told Timmy as she handed him the clothes.

Johnnie was happy he missed his bus. There was still a little snow, and he knew his garbage lid was still in the corner where he left it yesterday.

Shalanda felt awful. She knew it was a hangover from the night before, and she hated herself for letting her friends use her.

"I gotta have some fun sometime," she told herself as an excuse. Just then the doorbell rang. Shalanda opened it and there was her neighbor, Linda.

"Do you have the two dollars I loaned you last week? I spent all my check yesterday and now I don't have any bus money."

Shalanda went to get her purse. Much to her surprise, the $4.32 she left yesterday was gone. She knew her drunken friends had stolen it while she was passed out. Shalanda thought of the $20 she kept in her bra and told Linda she would get it for her by 2 o'clock.

At noon the mailman brought a surprise bill from the water company with a notice saying the water would be shut off if the $17.00 bill wasn't paid by the 15th. Shalanda thought of the $20 in her bra. She thought about Timmy's present, the dirty clothes, and Linda. She walked four blocks to the Un-Bank to get the right change for the watercompany.

Shalanda stuffed some of the change back in her bra and put the rest in her purse. She was heading back toward home when she met three guys. They walked past her and then suddenly lunged at her from behind. They ripped her purse away from her and ran, leaving her bruised and shaken.

Shalanda was grateful she wasn't hurt badly and could still walk home. When she got there, she took the money from her bra: seven one-dollar bills. She stuffed five of them back in her bra and hurried across the yard to pay Linda.

When she returned, she noticed the water bill on the table, shook her head despairingly and stuffed it on the shelf by the coffee mugs.

A couple days later, grandma went to make coffee and there was no water. Shalanda knew she'd have to go to the streets that night and sell her body. How she hated that, but she didn't know what else to do since she was too proud to beg.

In the meantime, her children kept getting dirtier and dirtier and the body odor became more and more unbearable. Then on Wednesday, Timmy came home to announce he was never going to that school again.

"Those guys called me a sewer rat," Timmy cried, as he buried his head in his dirty arms.

Grandma suggested they sell the kitchen table and chairs. She knew a family that would buy them for $15. By evening, the table and chairs were gone. Shalanda stuffed the money and another two dollars in the water bill envelope and ran to the mailbox. She was glad no postage was necessary.

Timmy didn't go to school the next day. He hid in his bedroom. Finally, two days later, the water was turned on. Shalanda put some dish soap in the bathtub and filled it full of soapy warm water. Both Johnnie and Timmy got to play in the warm soapy water all morning. Then, Shalanda washed some underpants and socks before she let the water run down the drain. She found some oversized clothes in a bag in a corner of the room which would have to do while their's were drying.

The next day, Shalanda woke up early to be sure Johnnie caught his Head Start bus, now that he had clean clothes. She brushed Timmy's hair and assured him everything would be O.K. Then she kissed his clean face and sent him to his bus.

"After school, you'll get your birthday present," she promised him.

Grandma was feeding the baby when she came back. Shalanda checked her bra for the remaining five dollars.

"Mom, I'm going to walk to the store and get Timmy a present."

She was so happy the toy car he wanted was marked down to $2.98. What a big thank you hug Shalanda received from her son that day!

Before Shalanda went to the streets, she had something to talk to her mom about. More and more, she had seen her reading the Bible, and was wondering about something.

"Mom, I didn't think you could read, yet I see you readin' the Bible. How you explain that?" Shalanda asked.

"Honey, ah don't know how He helps me. Jesus is my friend and I call on Him. He sees me through each day. You ought to have Him, then you wouldn't have to go to the demons every night," replied her mom so matter-of-factly.

Shalanda wished she could believe Jesus would solve all her problems, as she brushed three roaches from their makeshift table. She had no intention of falling for all that sweet and easy talk.

Shalanda dressed in her whore clothes. She hoped some pimp would want her because she desperately needed the money.

The next couple of hours were spent avoiding police, hiding in shadows of lamp posts, and finally being hustled by a stranger. Just as they were hurrying down the alley between 7th and Arlington, gun shots rang out ahead. They laid on the ground until all was quiet. Then they crept into the shadows, hugged the brick wall, and peered into the street light.

There in the light, Shalanda saw her own brother lying in a pool of blood. He'd been gunned down. She rushed to him, picked up his head and whispered, "Good-bye, Tony." Yes, it was true, her little brother was dead. Mom had told him not to join the Vice Lords, but because his friends did, Tony did, and now he was gone.

Shalanda heard the door of the ambulance slam and knew there was nothing more she could do. Struggling to control her anguish, she asked her pimp to walk her home.

When she got home, Shalanda woke her mom and told her what happened. Her mom slowly got out of bed, dropped to her knees, buried her head in her poor worn hands and cried, "Lord Jesus, have mercy. Lord Jesus, have mercy."

The funeral would be Thursday. Shalanda's biggest concern was what to wear. There'd be lots of people, and they'd all be looking at her and the kids. She decided to buy the boys suits on "layaway" and "lift" the clothes for the baby. They could be easily tucked in her shopping bag after she got the suits. As for herself, she thought she might get one of her street friends to give her some crack to sell tonight. Then tomorrow she'd buy the dress and sell it afterwards to pay back her friends.

After Shalanda returned from shopping, she was very tired. She felt lucky she made her get away without anyone seeing her. At least the kids would look nice. When her Mom asked her how she got the clothes, she told her not to worry about it. Shalanda heard her whisper, "Lord, have mercy."

After a short nap, Shalanda dressed in her whore clothes and took off into the shadows of the dark alley. She hid in "her place" and hoped they'd come. In minutes, three of them came. She told them she needed some crack to sell. They were happy to oblige. After all, Shalanda was their friend.

Shalanda knew where her addict friends hung out. She crawled along walls and hid behind cans, then ran into a basement under the steps of an apartment. There she found them--all needing a fix. She told the addicts she'd give them some crack if they gave her money, then she made her collections. Within minutes she had $60, which she put it in her bra and dashed out.

Shalanda knew she'd have to catch a bus before a pimp caught her and stole her money. How relieved she was to catch the last bus! She stumbled into the house, quickly locked the door, and went to bed in her bra to protect her precious money.

The next day Shalanda found a dress on sale for $49.00. Now she'd be ready for her brother's funeral. The exterminator met her at the door, as she came up the walk. "Do you have the stuff out of the cupboards?" he asked.

"No, but we will have," Shalanda answered. "You know you'll have to leave until evening after I spray," he explained.

Shalanda pulled the stuff from the shelves, piled it on the floor and in the corners, and covered it up with a sheet. Then she gathered up her baby and boys, and she and grandma walked to the park. After a few swings, Shalanda and her mom decided they should head to the church where they could get free meals. It was a long way, but they had all afternoon.

At last, exhausted, they arrived at the church. Suburban ladies were bringing in food and would soon be serving it. The boys could hardly wait. In the meantime, they went over to check out the fire alarm and an old organ. At last, it was time.

Shalanda held the baby and handed the boys each a plate. A nice lady came along to help. At last the whole family had their plates and big glasses of milk, too.

Grandma bowed her head to thank her Jesus. Shalanda, too, was thankful for the food and a place to rest. After they finished, they were told they had to leave since others would need their table. Shalanda took the sleeping baby. The two boys followed grandma, and slowly they made their way back to their sprayed but roach-free apartment.

Grandma set the alarm for 6 o'clock. There'd be lots to do before the family could get to Tony's funeral. It still didn't seem possible her baby boy was gone. At 17, he really didn't have a chance to learn what life was all about. "Lord, have mercy," she prayed over and over until she fell asleep.

The shrill alarm woke everyone, even baby Rosalee. The boys thought it was fun to put on their new suits. Shalanda tucked in their old tee shirts so they wouldn't show. Having fed and bathed the baby, she, too, got to wear her new "lifted" outfit. Grandma kept wondering how Shalanda got it and kept praying, "Lord, have mercy." At last, it was time to catch the bus for the funeral.

Lines of Vice Lords flanked the walk. They were dressed in their colors. Shalanda and grandma led the boys to the front. Johnnie asked if Uncle Tony was sleeping. Shalanda wondered why they didn't put a tie on him. Grandma just kept praying, "Lord, have mercy." She touched Tony's cold hand and wished he could say, "Good-bye, Mama." Then, through the wails and tears, the family was escorted to some front row seats.

Row after row of seats were filled with gang members. Slowly the line of Vice Lords filed past their dead comrade. Each one seemed to want to communicate, to say one more word. Some brushed away tears. Finally, their rows of empty seats were filled again.

Grandma clung to her Bible. When no minister showed up, Shalanda kept hoping grandma would offer a prayer.

After the reviewal line was gone, the undertaker read the obituary and quietly closed the casket. The wailing continued as family, relatives, friends, and Vice Lords filed from the funeral parlor. Afterwards, the undertaker then called the family to the office to tell them Tony's body would be stored in the freeze until the funeral bill was paid. When they arrived home, grandma decided to call Tony's father and tell him to come for the body. He could bury him on the family farm in Arkansas. Shalanda called United Way to ask if they could help with funeral expenses. They said they'd help, but she must pay half.

Shalanda made the boys change their clothes when they returned home. As she hung up their suits, she wondered if she could sell them and use the money to pay the layaway bill.

The cupboards needed scrubbing, and both grandma and Shalanda seemed glad to be busy, especially since their hearts were filled with so much sorrow. Why was life so hard in the city? Would it have been better to stay in Arkansas? What happened to all the dreams of the good life they had in their earlier years? Questions kept coming, but there were no answers. At last, all the dishes, pots, and pans were back in the cupboards, and grandma, Shalanda, and all three children went to bed after a very weary day.

The shrill of the phone woke Shalanda. It was Timmy's school calling. Since no one came for Parent-Teacher Conferences, one of the parents needed to report to the office before Timmy could go back to school. Shalanda said she hadn't known about it. Grandma then awoke and said Timmy had brought a note, but she couldn't read it and put it by the phone, then forgot to give it to Shalanda.

The next morning, when Shalanda caught the bus with Timmy, he buried his head in his jacket collar. It was embarrassing to have his mom go to school with him and even take him to the Principal's office.

Timmy started to cry as he said, "The other kids will think I've been bad. They already think I'm a sewer rat and now this."

Tears flowed down Timmy's cheeks. He wanted to run away. Once in the office, the Principal was nice. He told Timmy he was sorry about his uncle and that he could take his mom to the classroom and show her his work. Shalanda followed Timmy down the hall. Mrs. Petersen met them at the door. She told Timmy how happy she was to see him and showed them the art work on the bulletin board. A volunteer at the office offered to take Shalanda home.

"Can we go to church now that we have suits?" Timmy asked his Mom.

Grandma looked at Shalanda, and together they decided it was a good idea before she resold the suits. They planned to all go to church on Sunday morning. Timmy and Johnnie thought going to church would be fun until the man in the front they called "preacher" didn't know when to stop hollering. Timmy thought he used God's name too much. Johnnie kept wondering when they were going to get something to eat. At last, the church bus brought them back home. The boys never asked to go to church again.

A bill from layaway and one from the phone company came in the mail the same day as an important letter from the welfare office. At least that's what it said in big bold letters on the envelope.

Shalanda ran across the street to Linda's. She depended on her to help her read official mail.

"Before issuing your next check, it will be necessary for you to report to the welfare office and be checked for eligibility, " Linda read.

"Oh, my," Shalanda sighed. "What kind of a story am I going to have to tell them now?"

Shalanda took her place in the back of the line. She estimated there were only about 75 people. She was glad she hadn't brought the children, though lots of people brought them to prove eligibility. Shalanda knew the computer already had all that information.

Two hours later, Shalanda's number was called. She was led into a small office. The tired-looking clerk asked her for her birth date. Shalanda quickly told her and sure enough, the machine had all sorts of information about her.

"We're just checking to see if we have everything correct," said the clerk. She read off names, birthdays, address, telephone, and then she inquired about the fathers of the children. Shalanda was not able to tell the whereabouts of Johnnie and Timmy's father. He hadn't been seen since he appeared on Shalanda's porch the day she brought Johnnie home. He had come to pick up his deal pay, then disappeared forever. As for Rosalee's father, Shalanda knew his first name was Ray and that he lived on the streets. She met him there one night. She said she gave him his last payment last month and didn't plan to see him again.

"Shalanda, the government wants you to go back to school. You have two years to get your G.E.D. When did you drop out?" asked the weary clerk.

"I haven't been in school since Timmy was born. He was seven years old last month. I was in 9th grade in high school when I got pregnant."

"You have no choice if you wish to receive checks for the next two years," explained the lady. "There are classes in this building every weekday and three evenings. You can start anytime. Be sure to register at the office. Do you have someone who could care for your children?"

"Yes, my mother is living with us now. She moved in with us this past summer," Shalanda informed her. Shalanda thanked the tired lady and went out into the street, dazed over the sudden news of going back to school.

All the way home on the bus, Shalanda wondered how she could manage a home, crowd four years of high school into two years, then get a job. She decided it was too much to worry about, and instead would live one day at a time. Shalanda knew if her next check came on time, she'd pay off almost all her debts, even the layaway, except, of course, Tony's funeral bill.

Her check did come with a registration blank for classes. Shalanda asked Linda to help her fill it out. They noticed it said she was to report to class on November 10th. That was next week!

Shalanda left for school before the boys did. Grandma would have to see them off.

When Shalanda heard about all the reading the first instructor was requiring and learned of a test after the first week, she became frightened. "Don't they know I can't read above a third-grade level? Well, they'll find out," she said to herself.

Shalanda opened her first text. She knew it was called American History. The assignment was on the story of Harriet Tubman. She wanted to read it because she knew it was about one of her kind. She had heard her mother tell the story of the Underground Railroad. It seemed to Shalanda her own grandma was part of that story somehow. She looked down at the first page. The words were all blurred. She couldn't read anything! Was it because she didn't know the words, or was something wrong with her eyes? Tears filled her eyes as she tried again. They dropped onto the page with a splash.

Shalanda quickly wiped them away. The teacher noticed her and came over.

The teacher put her hand on Shalanda's shoulder and asked, "Is something wrong?"

"I can't see. Everything is blurred," Shalanda cried.

The teacher told her to leave and go down the hall to the school office. There, the principal let Shalanda call the medical center and make an appointment. She learned she couldn't get an appointment for two weeks. The teacher told her to come to classes anyway and listen.

Shalanda looked forward to getting her new glasses. How good it would be to see! If only she could read.

On Thursday, Shalanda went to get her new glasses. Yes, she could see better, but no, she still couldn't read! As Shalanda continued with classes, she found herself listening more than reading and wondered if she could pass the test. How could she read the questions? Shalanda decided to tell Mrs. Walsh she couldn't read. Mrs. Walsh gave her a tutor who spent an hour with her every Tuesday. Mrs. Walsh also told Shalanda she'd read the test questions for her and she could answer them aloud. Bit by bit, Shalanda struggled through the first course and received a passing grade. For the first time in her life, Shalanda was proud of her accomplishment.

Then the week of Christmas came. Johnnie's teacher sent home a brand new coat for him. It still had the tag on it. Shalanda thought she'd sell it and buy Christmas presents. She knew she could easily sell it. She'd go to the crack dealer and give him the coat in return for the drug. Then she'd take the crack out to addicts as she'd done before. In forty-five minutes, Shalanda received $135, put all the money in her bra, and headed south to Washington Street. There she found the big Toys 'R Us Store. Quickly, she picked out $120 worth of toys and a $10 scarf for grandma. Shalanda caught the bus and was glad to get home before the boys returned from school.

Since Johnnie had been put in all-day Kindergarten, it was much easier to keep track of her boys. Shalanda hid the toys under her bed and went to see what grandma had fixed for lunch. Much to her amazement, she didn't find a thing--not even a pan of cornmeal mush. Shalanda poked her head in grandma's room and found her in bed. "Ya'll sick?" she asked.

"Yes, I am. It's in my stomach," groaned grandma.

Shalanda knew her mother needed medical attention. Her color hadn't been good for a long time. Just then, Rosalee woke up and cried for her milk.

"After the boys get home, we'll all go to Emergency and see if they can tell you what's wrong," explained Shalanda.

Shalanda knew she'd have to spend the rest of her money for bus fares, but now that she had Christmas presents, the most important stuff was taken care of. Perhaps someone would give them food over Christmas. People always want to do good then. Shalanda called the church they went to once and put her name in for a basket. They asked if there was a man in the family. Shalanda told them "yes;" after all, Ray was still around somewhere. The fact he slept on her porch just last month meant he lived there. "Anyway," Shalanda thought, "those folks don't understand." She didn't want to tell them too much. She asked if they deliver, and they told her the man could get it the day before Christmas.

Grandma wanted to tell her grandsons the story of Jesus' birthday, but she knew Shalanda wouldn't want her pushing her religion on her kids.

The trip to Emergency was long and hard. It isn't easy to take two energetic boys, a fussing baby, and a sick grandma on a crowded bus where everyone and their packages jostle for a few empty seats. Neither Shalanda nor her mother had the energy to compete, so they remained standing toward the back.

At last, they arrived downtown, and the driver shouted, "Everyone off! This is the end of the line."

The walk to Emergency was only two blocks, but to Shalanda and her mom, it seemed like two miles. The attendants quickly fetched grandma a wheelchair when they saw her pale face.

They rushed her into an examination room. Shalanda waited in the lobby with her two energetic boys and fussing baby. After about an hour, a doctor came out to tell Shalanda her mom had cancer and it was in its last stages. He said there was nothing they could do for her.

When they wheeled grandma out, she was smiling. "Did you hear the news? I'm about ready to go to the Kingdom. It won't be long now and I'll be praisin' the Lord with all my kin that loved Him, too," she told her family.

Shalanda will never forget that smile. "God, there has to be somethin' to that faith in the Lord," she found herself saying, and for a fleeting minute, Shalanda almost wished she had it.

"Pull your car up to the door, Madam," ordered the attendant.

"We don't have a car. We rode the bus down here," Shalanda told him.

"Well, there aren't anymore buses. I'll order an ambulance. The system will pay for it."

Shalanda was relieved. All the way home, grandma was smiling her baby smile and singing to herself, "I'm goin' home to my Jesus."

Grandma stayed in bed most of the time. Shalanda was glad she didn't have classes for two weeks. The boys had vacation, too. Shalanda wondered what she'd do when everything started up again. She decided she'd worry about that when it happened.

Shalanda opened the last can of soup, added lots of water and some beans from the previous meal. That would have to do for lunch. In two days, her next check would come. Shalanda knew she'd have to hide some money for pain medicine and bus fare. She wondered if maybe they'd let her skip classes for January.

Grandma's health kept getting worse as the winter days came and went. On the 22nd of January, Shalanda went in to see how she was, since she hadn't heard her in the bath all morning. She found grandma with her hands folded over her blanket. A smile shone on her face. Shalanda knew grandma was now in that Kingdom of Peace she often talked about.

Shalanda took the rest of grandma's Social Security money to bury her. It was a beautiful funeral. Shalanda had the preacher from church read grandma's favorite verses from the Bible. When he read, "The Lord is my shepherd, I shall not want," Shalanda's eyes filled with tears and she prayed, "Grandma, tell Jesus to come and be my friend, now" . . . and Shalanda was filled with peace.

Shalanda sold all their funeral clothes, even the baby's, after the funeral. She didn't have grandma to baby-sit now, so she'd have to find a place for Rosalee while she was at school. Shalanda was able to get enough money for the first two weeks. The day care was close to her school, so she could take Rosalee on the bus with her and drop her off.

Shalanda cashed her check after school on the 1st of February. Since she didn't have to pay Ray, there was a bit more. But after she paid for rent, utilities, and phone, there was a whole lot less. She bought food stamps and hurried to the market, pushing Rosalee in the carriage a school friend gave her. Shalanda and Rosalee arrived home just as the school bus pulled up to the corner.

Both Johnnie and Timmy ran to help their mom. They knew there'd be something in those bags for them to eat. As they licked the popsicle, Shalanda noticed how dirty their clothes were. How could she ever keep up! And there wasn't even enough money left for the laundromat!

Shalanda put the groceries away. Then, exhausted, she sat down to think. Instead of thinking, she found herself praying, "The Lord is my shepherd, I shall not want."

Again, the feeling of peace came over her. She whispered, "Jesus, come and be my friend." Then she imagined herself in a flower garden and Jesus came over to her, took her hand, and led her over a little bridge. In His gentle and kind voice, He said, "Here is My Kingdom, Shalanda. I want you to give up all your evil ways, the lies, the stealing, the drugs, the alcohol, and the sex. Trust Me to be your friend, and I'll show you the Way."

Shalanda lifted her head. There she was, back with her children in her living room. She went over to raise the shade on the west window. Sunlight came streaming in. It made everyone feel happy and warm. Even baby Rosalee laughed as she clapped her hands in the sunbeams.

"Tomorrow is Saturday. None of us have school, so we're going to the Thrift Store to find come church clothes," Shalanda told her children.

"What, we goin' to church again!" Timmy exclaimed.

The boys didn't seem very enthusiastic. They were remembering their past experience.

"You'll have a surprise, you just wait and see," Shalanda told them. She didn't have the slightest idea what it might be, but she believed Jesus was now her friend and He'd provide.

Sunday morning, everyone was up early. The boys looked so clean and scrubbed in their new thrifty clothes. Baby Rosalee was so cute in her ruffled dress with the matching panties. They arrived at church early, so the lady who greeted them showed them around. She showed them the baby room where Rosalee would be cared for. She showed them the classroom where the boys could learn the Commandments, Bible verses, and the story of Jesus. She told them classes started next Sunday for a half hour before services. Then Shalanda asked if she could learn. She told her that no one had ever taught her. The lady said she'd be glad to teach her herself.

Just then, the church bell rang. The boys ran to see how it worked. The man even let them hang onto the rope as he rang it.

The lady escorted Shalanda and the boys up to the front where they could see. The preacher started reading from the Bible. He began with, "The Lord is my shepherd, I shall no want."

"Hey, Mom," Timmy whispered to his Mother, "they're sayin' your prayer!"

"I know," Shalanda whispered. Her eyes were filled with tears of joy.

The preacher welcomed Shalanda and her boys. He had them stand and take a bow. Everyone clapped. The boys thought that was great. Afterwards, the preacher invited everyone to a party in the Social Room.

Timmy and Johnnie liked the doughnuts. Shalanda met another new friend. Her name was Gracie. Gracie told Shalanda she lived on Rochester Street. Shalanda thought it was wonderful to have someone from church as her neighbor only one street over.

After the services, Gracie told Shalanda she'd drop them off since she had a car. Shalanda thanked her new friend and told her to plan to come over after service next Sunday to have lunch with them. Gracie was pleased and accepted the invitation.

It wasn't long before Shalanda and Gracie were good friends. They shared so much, the good and the not so good.

When Shalanda ran out of food, she invited Gracie to go with her and the children to Loaves and Fishes. While they were being served the good hot meal, they wondered how it would be if they offered to serve next time. They asked, and the ladies said they'd be glad to have them help. It wasn't long before Betty and Lucille, the suburban ladies, were asking if they could eat with them. By now, the table in the corner had really "come alive." No one asked them to hurry and eat. As they lingered over their coffee, they were finding so much to share. In fact, Gracie and Shalanda suggested their churches share garage sales this spring. Since each church had a sale in March, one weekend it would be at Holy Redeemer and the next at Good Shepherd.

How much fun those sales were! Shalanda was able to pick out whatever she could use just because she was helping. She even found a table and chairs for her kitchen. "Yes, the Lord is my Shepherd," prayed Shalanda.

When Betty found out Shalanda's tutor had to quit because she was going to have a baby, she offered to teach Shalanda.

Betty would come every Tuesday evening at 6:30. Shalanda was so happy she had a kitchen table. She let the boys have the other table. Betty's daughter came, too, to play school with the boys.

At last Shalanda would be graduating. The two years had gone by quickly. Shalanda had surprised herself on how well she could read by now. With Jesus as her shepherd, it seemed what used to be thought of as impossible was now possible. Even Rosalee went to watch her Mom get her diploma. The boys liked the party afterwards.

When one school friend congratulated Shalanda and asked, "Now what are your dreams?" Shalanda hardly knew what to answer. She'd been so busy trying to reach her graduation goal, she didn't let herself think past that.

"I'm not sure. But there's one thing I know. Nothing's impossible with the Good Shepherd. If He gives the dream, He'll fulfill it."

Shalanda surprised herself with what she was saying. Did she really believe what she found herself saying? Yes, and as she displayed her diploma on the mantle, she looked up at the picture of the Good Shepherd Gracie had given her and prayed. "Jesus, my Lord, help me know what You want. Mom, tell Jesus to show me the way."

By the time Timmy finished first grade, he was trying to sound out and read everything. Shalanda listened as he attempted to sound out the words on the cereal boxes for his little brother. Then she realized if all three of them spent some time together, they could help each other. Gracie gave Shalanda some books her kids had already read. Together, they read them all. Reading time became a fun time for all three. The three of them looked forward to going to school and learning more.

Shalanda called Betty, her suburban friend, to ask if she'd help her find a job. Betty was thrilled to be asked. She knew Shalanda would do well with whatever job she had. Together, they scanned the want ads and took down phone numbers and addresses. They went to three places, all of them handed out application blanks and said they'd call.

After that, Betty took Shalanda for a sandwich and some coffee. In the restaurant, Shalanda said, "Betty, I know the Lord will provide, but let's ask Him for help."

The two of them bowed their heads. Moments later, Shalanda had an idea.

"Betty, I'm a mother. I know how to care for children. Doesn't your church have a Day Care for little ones?"

"Yes, they do, and who knows, maybe they need help. Come on, let's go find out," responded Betty enthusiastically.

Together, they drove over to Good Shepherd Church. The little ones were all napping so the Director spoke to them in a whisper.

"Please come in."

They wound their way through the cots with the sleeping children and into the side office.

"Jane, this is Shalanda. She's a friend of mine and mother of three little children. Could you use help in any way with your children here," Betty asked.

"Oh Betty, you don't know what a gift you are to me," the Director answered. "One of our teachers had to leave because her husband was transferred. Why don't you come, Shalanda, and be a volunteer helper for awhile? Then we'll see if you can be hired as a teacher."

Shalanda was thrilled, but wondered to herself how she'd be a volunteer when she'd have all those bills to pay!

"The Lord is my Shepherd," she whispered and wanted to believe what seemed then to be the impossible.

As Betty drove Shalanda home, she spoke of how happy she was Shalanda would be at their church, and told her their church was serving that night at Loaves and Fishes.

That evening, Betty, Lucille, and two new friends from Good Shepherd joined Shalanda and her family at the table in the corner. As they ate their hot meal together, Shalanda told them of her financial concern, but how happy she'd be to be a volunteer at their Day Care.

Afterwards, the four Good Shepherd ladies who listened to Shalanda's concerns decided they'd discuss with their husbands some possibilities. Lucille's husband was a Deacon in the Church, and Agnes's husband was one of the Financial Committee members. They decided "mission" should begin at home and their Church should give loans to people like Shalanda instead of making "handouts" to people they don't even know. After all, one half of the tithing money was used for missions and what better mission could there be than helping one family at a time?

Agnes and her husband offered to help Shalanda budget her money so all her bills could be paid as they came due. They also kept track of what she owed the church, so that someday she could give it back to help another family.

One day, after Sunday Services, Gracie and Shalanda were recounting how much fun they had with their friends at the garage sales.

All of a sudden, Gracie said, "Shalanda, you know what we could do? Let's have a family picnic in the park and enjoy all the families from our table at Loaves and Fishes. The kids could play on the swings, and grown-ups could share around a table. Everyone could bring a hot dish and one other thing to share."

Shalanda quickly agreed. They set the Sunday date and planned the invitations. Together, they'd invite the families the next Monday, when they saw them at Loaves and Fishes.

The sun shone brightly the Sunday of the picnic. Johnnie and Timmy were excited. This would be their first family picnic. They were eager to meet their new Good Shepherd friends, too.

After Shalanda helped the boys with their plates, she fixed little Rosalee's. Then she was able to enjoy the good food and friendship herself.

"Yes, the Lord does provide," she said aloud.

All the folks around that table agreed. Shalanda watched as the husbands sat with their wives and helped them with their little ones. She also noticed how they teased each other and how happy they all seemed.

When Shalanda returned home, she couldn't help but think about those husbands. "Lord, do you have a husband for me, now that I'm Yours?" she prayed.

Shalanda no more than said the prayer when she remembered Ray. She recalled how she always looked forward to his coming each month, and for nine months. Then there was nothing. She wondered what he was doing now. Yes, she'd like him for a husband forever.

"Lord," she prayed, "Your will be done."

The next day, Shalanda was at the supermarket. Her bags would be too many and too heavy to take the bus. She looked over at the men sitting there waiting for some $3.00 business. There was Ray!

"Ray, would you like to take me home?" she asked as little Rosalee peeked around her legs.

"Oh yes, Madam," Ray said politely. "It would be a privilege, and look at my little girl!" He took Rosalee in his arms and gave her a big daddy hug.

When they arrived home, Shalanda invited Ray in for some coffee and a visit. They had so much catching up to do. Shalanda told Ray how she'd become a Christian and how Jesus changed her life. She told him how she wanted him, the father of her baby, to be her husband. She told him, how she felt the Lord had brought them back together in love.

Ray said he, too, felt attracted to Shalanda, but he wanted to respect her. Shalanda explained to him they shouldn't have any more sex until after they were married, and that they should be married in a Christian church, and united in the Lord. She explained how this is a lifetime promise and the Lord would bless them and their children.

Shalanda and Ray visited into the night, long after the children were fast asleep. Never once did Shalanda and Ray bring up the subject of finances. Maybe it was because Shalanda kept saying, "How good the Lord is!" and "He does provide!"

She told him how, since she became a Christian, everything was working out for her. How she doesn't have problems now to solve. Instead, she now has her new life to live!

Ray came to Shalanda often after that. They'd spend their evenings taking walks in the park or holding hands on the swing on the front porch. No one was surprised when the news broke that Shalanda and Ray were to be married at the Redeemer Church on Saturday, June 12th. Shalanda invited all her friends from the church, her neighbors, and the friends from Good Shepherd Church, too. She also invited her tutor and teachers from the school.

The boys would be ring bearers. There'd be one ring for Ray and another for Shalanda. Rosalee would be the flower girl. Agnes and her husband helped Shalanda budget some money for her wedding. There'd be enough for a simple dress and veil and a new suit for Ray. Shalanda's friends had some fine clothes for the children. Good Shepherd Church donated flowers. There'd be a picnic pot luck in the city park afterwards. Everyone who brought a dish was invited.

What a glorious day it was! The wedding was so special. As the choir sang "Amazing Grace," both Shalanda and Ray cried and squeezed each other's hands. How beautiful to be in love with the Lord!

The children seemed extra happy. Now they'd have a real daddy, and now they had a real family!

That evening, Shalanda and Ray played with their three children and knew their dreams had come true. When they went to bed that night, they could feel the Lord's love and peace enfold them.

One week after the wedding, Shalanda received the good news that she'd become a full-time staff member of the Good Shepherd Day Care Center. Oh! How happy she was! Now she could begin paying back the church what she owed, so it could help someone else. Agnes and Deacon Ed helped her know that in just six months she'd be able to start her own savings account.

Ray and Shalanda, now Mrs. and Mrs. Brown, continued going for their evening strolls, hand in hand. They'd recount the Lord's blessings, talk about their children, and as days grew into weeks, they began dreaming together. Yes, Ray was happy with his new job at the lumber yard, but he only worked twenty hours a week. Then he told Shalanda about the Habitat for Humanity Program where couples can help build their own home, then own it with a low mortgage. Shalanda and Ray didn't know much about mortgages, but Shalanda thought Agnes and Deacon Ed could help them learn. She told Ray to check into it.

Two weeks later, a call came from Habitat. They wanted to visit with Ray and Shalanda. How happy Ray and Shalanda were when they saw some friends from Good Shepherd at the meeting as well as the Habitat officials. A plan was made that Ray and Shalanda would begin to help build their home on July 22nd. Since Shalanda had a full-time job, she'd be expected to work on Saturdays, and Ray in his off-time during the week. Both Shalanda and Ray learned a lot from the Habitat people. Gracie offered to baby-sit while Shalanda was working on the house. On June 24th, the following year, Mr. and Mrs. Brown and their three children moved into their new home. Both Holy Redeemer and Good Shepherd churches gave them a house shower. That evening, Shalanda noticed on her calendar that June 24th was the feast of the Good Shepherd. The whole family knelt together to thank and praise the Lord for their new home and ask His blessing. Then they recited together their favorite Psalm, The Lord is My Shepherd.

Timmy brought the notice of parent-teacher conferences home. Shalanda was so glad she could read it. She signed up to go with Ray on Monday evening, 6:30. Gracie would care for the children. It was so good to hear both of their boys were doing well in school. The only problem seemed to be that some of the non-church kids were making fun of them. Next evening, the whole family prayed for all the children who hadn't yet realized the Lord is their Shepherd, too.

Because Shalanda had to leave at 6:00 a.m. with Rosalee, Ray learned quickly how to give two little boys their breakfast and send them off to school. The morning ride on the bus afforded Shalanda a chance to praise the Lord for all His blessings, while Rosalee continued her early morning sleep.

Ray and Shalanda knew this Easter would be especially glorious. Not only was it the first anniversary of their marriage, but they asked Pastor Paul if they could all be baptized that day as a family. The prayers, ceremony, and church friends all made the Brown family know they truly belonged to the family of the Holy Redeemer.

Ray and Shalanda pooled their savings each month, and with Agnes and Deacon Ed's continued help, they were able to pay all their bills, even the mortgage on the house.

When the lumber company told Ray they were going to advance him to a 40-hour-a-week job, he was delighted. It meant he, too, would have to leave the house at 6:00 a.m.

Ray and Shalanda wondered how it might be to have a student come and live with them. They asked Lucille and Betty to see if there might be a college girl from their church who'd be interested. The following Tuesday, Sylvia came to meet the family. She was happy to have a home close to the bus line. She was a sophomore at the University and was majoring in social work.

The Browns found Sylvia a wonderful addition to their family. She was like a big sister. Shalanda wondered if they were doing enough for her in return for all she did for them. Besides being a fill-in for both Ray and herself, Sylvia seemed to sense when she was needed and offered her services. It was so wonderful having such a generous person living right in their home.

When Sylvia asked if she could join the family at their church services, Ray and Shalanda were thrilled. She soon fit right into the Holy Redeemer Church family, also.

Shalanda and Ray invited Sylvia's family over for dinner one Sunday evening. Since Sylvia had three brothers and two sisters all younger than herself, as well as her mother and father, they had to put two extra leaves in the table and put on their longest table cloth. Sylvia's father ran a car dealership. He and Ray had a lot to share about their work. Sylvia's mother and Shalanda had everything to talk about, especially how to make that great hot dish Shalanda had prepared.

Bob and Ann were given a first-class tour through the new home. They wished they had kitchen cupboards like theirs. Little did they know Ray had built them. After the tour, Ray offered to build some for their home if he could work on Saturdays.

Ray enjoyed building the cupboards for the Blackburns. Since he worked only on Saturdays, it took him two months. Finally, the day he was finished, Bob and Ann invited the whole Brown family to dinner in their home with the new homemade cupboards.

After dinner, Bob left the table and went outdoors. Soon a car horn sounded. Ann went to the door. There was a shiny family van with a big bow on it!

"This is our gift to you. We'll pay the insurance for one year," Bob announced.

Shalanda and Ray were so stunned they could hardly say thank you. Ray said Shalanda and he would go and get their licenses the following week. On Wednesday, Shalanda let them know they both had their licenses. Bob and Ann drove over with the new car. Then, after a bit of celebrating in the backyard, Ray and Shalanda drove them back home.

The peony bush in the Brown's front yard was in full bloom. It was Memorial Day. Shalanda thought it would be nice to put some of the flowers on grandma's grave. The whole family, Sylvia, too, climbed into the van with their arms full of those wonderful blooms. They placed them on grandma's grave. Then everyone knelt to thank grandma for helping them find the Good Shepherd. By now, the whole family, even Rosalee, knew Psalm 23 by heart. While they recited that beautiful prayer, Shalanda imagined she could see grandma smiling and saying, "Yes, the Lord is your Shepherd, you shall not want."

The story of Shalanda challenges each of us. In Shalanda, we see a person who has not only been a victim of her environment and her past, but also a person who has fallen into moral degradation through her own desperate and wrong choices. She failed to take responsibility for her life because of her habitual dependency. It was only after other people crossed her path and were willing to take risks and reach out to her, that she began gradually taking on a new life.

Chapter IV

An Urgent Call to All

There's a universal invitation from our Creator, not only to those worshiping in synagogues, mosques, temples, and churches, but to people everywhere, to be concerned and care for all their brothers and sisters, including those who live, think, and believe differently. It's a call to reach out to those with no pillow for their heads or shoulders for their troubled hearts. It's a call to get acquainted with those who, day after day, live in the midst of every sort of degradation. It's a call to literally fall in love with the unwanted, impoverished, dead-enders, outcasts, losers, and forgotten.

When we love and serve without judgment, we love unconditionally and allow healing to happen. Then the broken connection between the world and God is mended, and a new sense of wholeness takes place. Love replaces the despair of failure with forgiveness. It reaches out, supports, sustains. The molten core of loving kindness is understanding. It's the capacity to empty oneself of one's own concerns to view things from inside someone else.

The universal invitation from our Creator encourages, finds, and creates ways of enabling us to care for others and encourage them to become responsible for their own lives. It means being with those in need in a thousand ways that seem too insignificant for naming. Yet, this is the kind of care needed for transforming others into a new life.

We need to recognize others, no matter what their situation. Like us, they're human beings with feelings, dreams, and aspirations. We believe in the power of tenderness, the strength of gentleness, and the warmth of a smile. We know the sun shines behind clouds, flowers grow between rocks, and there's a smile under tears. More than ideas, gifts, and answers, this call to assist others gives people back the gift of themselves. Love is the spirit that guides people to recognize their own creative potential and find ways to touch and transform human life around them in new and imaginative ways

Chapter V

The "How" of Charity - A Meditation

Working With the Poor

Perhaps the time has come for us to realize we can no longer do charity by working for the poor or going to them. We need to change our prepositions and start working with the poor. Yes, it's the human contact in this world that counts.

Mission isn't bringing Jesus to people, but recognizing where He already is. We must believe all people are beautiful. We believe Jesus has already come. He has created, redeemed, and loved. We know His Love continues. Our challenge is to help make His Love, which is already here, become real.

Believing in People

It's amazing what happens when people start believing in people. A whole new world unfolds before them. They begin sensing within themselves powers and talents they didn't know they had. Once people are aware of their inner worth, they become energized from within. This inner energy is the motivation from which springs positive action. Life begins to take on newer and fuller meaning.

Our Faith doesn't free us to do away with suffering or find quick cures, but gives us courage to enter into solidarity with the weak, vulnerable, lonely, and broken.

It's easy to become ensnared by power and riches. A church wanting to call itself a Missionary Church finds itself hard of hearing when conscience speaks. Jesus, our Model, shows us the Way. He came not to be ministered to, but to give and serve. Only when we have need of His Love can we become compassionate. Only when we empty ourselves, can we share in the riches of a personal relationship.

Love of God Through Neighbor

In Christianity, love of neighbor is the way we express our love of God. Love of God without love of neighbor is full of illusions. It's too easy to think of God according to our own image and likeness. God is silent. He lets us do as we wish. But neighbors don't let us treat them as we wish. They need our love and can be very demanding.

Christians Are a Community

Together, Christians are a community of struggling, suffering, doubting, seeking people on a pilgrimage to the Father. Jesus is being repeatedly crucified in the world. Christians can't afford to pass Him by or look on from a safe distance. Jesus has given us His Life and Love to reach out and change what we touch. The Divine Breath will breathe new life into our human limitations, and we'll be filled with quiet reverence as we experience the tenderness of a new relationship and recognize God as both Giver and Gift.

PART II

Introduction To Part II

Need For Maintaining Morality

People of good will needn't wallow in a world of darkness. We're people of peace. We know our treasure lies within us, giving us power to transform our neighborhoods, schools, homes, and churches.

We're indeed in the midst of a dreadful, unseen, moral war. God has become cut off from His own creation. His influence has become an illegal and unwanted intrusion into people's privacy. Moral values that have been the very foundation of our civilization are now being questioned and rejected. Because our Constitution was founded upon the recognition of God's existence, our rights are inalienable. Now, in some people's minds, Divine Law has become not only irrelevant, but unlawful. It's believed to restrict people's freedom, and, therefore, shouldn't be used as a consideration in making laws or standards of moral behavior. If immorality is allowed to replace solid values, the whole moral fiber of our civilization will crumble.

Each Person's Transforming Power

If there ever was a time in history when our world needed hope, it's now. We need to sit down with each other. Having believed in ourselves, we can now believe in a transforming power within each person. We can begin discussing creatively and unthreateningly ideas that can instill in us a new enthusiasm and courage.

Ideas presented in Part II are meant for that purpose. They may seem idealistic for our own individual, day-to-day situations, but let's begin with the idealistic, and, for a better tomorrow, and after listening to each other, decide what we each can use right now.

Chapter I

The Neighborhood

For our purposes here, we'll think of our neighborhood as the geographical area surrounding our home on all sides, whether next door, or across the street or alley.

From Shalanda's story, we understand the need for healthy and empowering relationships. These relationships can be found in our own neighborhoods. Our first task is to assume responsibility for becoming acquainted with everyone in our neighborhood.

Since there's no busing of school children, parents and grandparents will be taking children to their neighborhood school on a regular basis, giving them the opportunity to become acquainted with other children and each other. Socials should be organized within each neighborhood to afford additional opportunities for coming together and getting to know each other better. These shouldn't be problem-solving meetings, but friendly, positive gatherings where everyone comes to know each other as friends.

A few ideas for Socials are suggested below.

Potluck Picnics

These should be in a nearby park. Neighbors can bring their own dishes and tableware. A fountain in the park can provide fresh water.

Box Social

Each family packs a box or basket for themselves plus one other surprise food item for another family. Each family is assigned a number which is put on their surprise bag; the family getting the surprise bag joins the family whose number is on that bag.

Honoring Helpers

This could be a pot luck where you invite the mailman, policeman who patrols your neighborhood, school teachers, and any volunteers who help make your neighborhood a better place to live. Once everyone is acquainted with everyone else in your neighborhood, you might try some of the socials describe below.

Celebrate Birthdays

Everyone who has a birthday in a given month could meet in the park at a particular time. By keeping the same date each month, communications can be kept to a minimum. Kids can be sent out ahead of time to notify everyone. Presents can be collected after Christmas when everyone gets too much. Put these gifts in a big grab bag, and give each honoree the privilege of drawing a surprise. If a gift doesn't fit, or there's something a person can't use, use it as a gift for another occasion.

Showers for Newlyweds

A wedding is a wonderful time for a neighborhood to come together and congratulate the happy couple. Each neighbor can bring some practical little gift for the new couple's home.

Showers for a New Baby

This works better after the baby has arrived. A small gift helps new parents know their baby is welcome in the neighborhood family. Relatives of the baby or neighbors can provide a simple dessert.

Welcome Party

This is an especially good time to help newcomers meet neighbors and come to know some events of the neighborhood. Neighbors can bring desserts or drinks. It can also be an appropriate time to show the latest video about recent neighborhood happenings, or provide some other update.

Farewells for Those Moving Away

It's important to make a memory for friends who move away. They should be notified in advance of a gathering in a nearby park or other meeting place. There doesn't need to be a meal. Simple cookies and drinks are fine. Instead of bringing going away gifts, neighbors can volunteer to baby-sit, help pack, bring a hot dish, or be on the Send-Off Committee.

Visits to the Sick and House-Bound

Once neighbors know each other, they'll learn to care about each other in time of sickness or when house-bound, or in trouble and need help. Ways people can care are unlimited. It isn't necessary to always come bearing gifts. What sick or lonely friends need more than anything is the gift of ourselves, though it's also an excellent time to share a few flowers from our garden.

Parades in the Park

These can be simple. Bicycles tied with crepe paper streamers, pinwheels, or balloons, and accompanied by music from a marching band recording, are lots of fun for youngsters. A line of dressed-up pets can also be fun. It 's better not to judge these, since we need to learn how to enjoy each other without criticism and judgment.

Gardens

These can be for both flowers and vegetables. Neighbors can help each other by sharing seeds, tools, and plants. Videos taken of gardens in summer can be shown during winter months. This is an excellent time to teach composting and other gardening hints. Also, vegetables and flowers could be sold at the local farm market, or the neighborhood could set up its own market in a park pavilion or other appropriate public place.

Annual Review

This is a neighborhood get together with police, firemen, teachers, and volunteers to learn important laws of the particular area or review other matters. Some subjects covered could be the Need for Curfews, Respect for Property, Annoyance of Loud Music, Prohibition of Public Urinating, Graffiti, Late Parties, etc. Laws can be stated or explained, violations and punishments read. These rules and punishments, together with a phone number to call to report violators, can be published on a public bulletin board in the park or other appropriate place.

Sports

Since there are no sports during the school academic day, they can usually be scheduled after school hours on school grounds or in a nearby park where there are outdoor drinking fountains. Athletic equipment can be brought from homes, and parents and kids can referee their own games. Cooperation, fairness, and safety at these events should be stressed over competition.

Yard Exchanges or Barters

Neighbors can bring articles of clothing, household items, or sports equipment (everyone limited to 3 items). These items can then be exchanged for others. No money need be used.

Car Pools and Baby-Sitting Gatherings

Those who have needs for car pools or baby-sitting meet with neighbors who can help or who know someone else who can. There could be service exchanges, also, instead of using money.

Talent Sharing

Neighbors and their friends share talents with other neighbors and friends. These are usually how-to-do-it sessions. Some suggestions: Carpenter Tips, Making Ceramics, Tortilla Making, Music, Dancing, Photography, or Jewelry Making.

Jobs in the Neighborhood

Anyone who has a job to be done can advertise on a park or other neighborhood bulletin board. It would be ideal to exchange services. For example, "I'll mow your yard, if you pick up my groceries." Neighbors can also get together to offer services to the home-bound and handicapped. Such services might include washing windows, raking, or mowing lawns.

The Library

Since education is a high priority for everyone in the neighborhood, it's appropriate to have a library centrally located and staffed with volunteers at least twelve hours a day. It's important to have a quiet reading room, too, and another room where children and adults can read aloud to each other, plus a story room for reading and listening. There could also be a room for creative play equipped with Legos and Tinker Toys. Appropriate magazines and newspapers can be available at tables in the front lobby. Books aren't checked out in this library. The city's Mobile Library is for that purpose. Also, the neighborhood Reading Library isn't to be used for socials. It's used only for education and should be respected for this purpose. Children should always be accompanied by adults.

Loaves and Fishes In Reverse

Inner city neighborhoods sponsor a potluck for suburban people, perhaps from some church, who wish to become acquainted as friends. It's important people mix and eat and share with each other. For example, a table of eight might have four from the suburbs and four from the inner city. Notepaper and pencils should be on each table so names, telephone numbers, and addresses can be shared. If potlucks can be continued consecutively, a better bonding of friends would occur. Many wonderful and unexpected things can happen as a result. Such results are evident in Shalanda's story.

Hardships and Tragedies

Neighbors who know each other as friends are quick to respond in times of sorrow. It's important persons needing help respond with gratitude and appreciation.

Good Citizen Award

Every year some person is selected from the neighborhood to receive a Good Citizen Award from the city. That person's name can then be printed in gold on a plaque and displayed in the park

Chapter II

The School

The neighborhood school, as described here, is oriented toward Community. Such a school would have been a tremendous support for Shalanda and her children when she was attempting to improve her choices. Also, a teacher, having met Shalanda in her home, would have understood much of the behavior of her sons.

As you approach the neighborhood school, you see two flags gracing the top of the flagpole. First, the American flag, and under it, the school flag. The school flag is white with an Eagle clutching a banner on which are the words, In God We Trust.

Again, as you enter the school, you see a large banner with the same words, In God We Trust. We believe it's necessary to acknowledge God as our Creator and Father before we can understand why we should love and respect ourselves, our brothers and sisters, and all others.

Unknowing persons can be taught to respect others and others' property by learning reasons to do so that make sense.

Such educationed understanding brings everything into focus, giving us a perspective on which to build a peaceful and fruitful future.

Schools should immediately begin morality instruction in grades K-6, adding 7th grade the following year, and 8th grade the third year if the instruction in all grades can't be started at once.

Suggested below are some guidelines.

Basic Moral Virtues

Every child in school must be taught moral virtues every year. The most basic virtues of courtesy and honesty must be taught in lower grades, the sooner the better. Later, virtues of responsibility and respect can be taught. Though living these virtues is expected, and students may have role models, no one should take the virtues for granted and assume they're merely taught. Daily practice is needed.

Principal and Teacher Residency

Principal and teachers are encouraged to reside in school neighborhoods. During the first month, the principal works at school, but teachers don't. Teachers are expected to visit each student's home, meet every parent, and invite parents into partnership for the education of their children.

Teachers must be paid for first month visitations, and their bonding progress shared weekly with the principal. By the end of the month, teachers should be well acquainted with their students, including students' families, pets, and home environments. How excited children will be when they know their teacher is their friend!

The School Community

Having spent a school month in their students' neighborhoods, teachers should feel at home there. This feeling of belonging is carried into school. It's shared with students, other teachers, and parents. Once the feeling of partnership is established, children are taught about School Pride and Respect. They begin taking ownership and come to a realization the school is their school.

Books

Books should be issued protective covers and covered by students. Covers, for example, should display our country's motto In God We Trust. Also, there should be two sets of books for each classroom. One set stays in the classroom; the other is placed in the city's Mobile Library to be used for homework.

Cooperative Learning

Older students help younger and handicapped children.

School Day

School days begin no earlier than 9 o'clock and end at 4 o'clock. This enables students to have breakfast at home with their families.

Dress Code

Students should wear a school uniform. A uniform for teachers can also be appropriate. Both teachers and students should wear a school emblem pin.

Lunchroom

Adult volunteers and older students help prepare noon lunch and wear aprons made by the sewing class. Older students also supervise the lunchroom.

All students eat with their teachers at round tables. They have a family-style meal, and are encouraged to use correct table manners.

Boys learn to push chairs in for girls. All learn to speak in low, soft voices, and no one leaves until all have finished and a prayer of thanksgiving said. Students take turns helping adult volunteers with serving and cleanup.

School Library

The library must have books for all age levels. These books aren't checked out, but used at the facility only. Children are taught to respect all books.

The library should have a Reading Room where older children can read aloud to younger ones. A separate room should be available for private reading. It's essential to maintain silence at all times.

Adult volunteers and older children act as librarians. There need be no card files, since all necessary encyclopedias and supplements are in the classroom. All books are arranged according to the alphabet.

The school library is for enjoying reading and learning, as well as for quiet study and homework.

Penmanship

This is of special importance in each classroom. Time must be allotted each day for practicing. The Palmer Method is used. Children who qualify become enrolled in the Pen Pal Club.

They have the privilege of corresponding with children throughout the United States.

Career Development

The Principal should invite local people to share stories about their work. They might be people from the grocery, gas station, post office, garbage dump, police department, fire station, farm, church, and hospital.

Mobile Library

Mobile Library vans need to visit each neighborhood every week day. Children and parents can be assisted with homework by retired teacher or other capable volunteers who can staff these vans. Books from the Mobile Library can be checked out for home use.

Nurse and Doctor

School nurse and doctor can be retired volunteers. They'd make home calls to visit with parents when necessary.

Janitor

Retired mechanics and machinists can help students keep their school clean and in good condition.

Carpenter Shop

Students can be assisted by retired carpenters to make items for their school such as tables, chairs, and bookcases.

Sewing Class

Students can make aprons for kindergartners, and for Lunchroom and Kitchen helpers.

Greenhouse Gardens

Students can raise flowers to be planted at their school around the flag pole and drinking fountain, for example. They might also create their own colorful flower garden on school grounds.

Exchanging Classes

Teachers of the same grades should exchange classes every other month. This helps unite the school community. It also lends variety for both teachers and students.

Affirmation Team

Retired teachers, parents, and grandparents, can form an Affirmation Team to visit classrooms and give positive affirmation to both students and teachers, as well as the principal and assistant volunteers.

Cleaning Responsibility

Students should be expected to help keep their school clean. Some of the jobs they can do are: clean classrooms, empty baskets, clean erasers and boards, sweep sidewalks, and wash windows.

Homework

Children need to have homework assignments every day. They must also take home all their mistakes. They'll be given assistance with corrections at the Mobile Library after school and during homework hour with their families. Every child should go to bed every evening knowing all work is done.

Salutations

Students must be taught to greet teachers each morning with respect. They should address teachers using last names, preceded by the appropriate, "Mr.," "Mrs.," or "Miss." At the end of each day, students should be taught to say, "Thank you, Mrs. Smith. May God bless you!" Students should also step aside in the halls or on stairs to let adults pass.

Appreciation Day

Once a year, students can sponsor an Appreciation Day, inviting the principal and all teachers and volunteers to a pot luck supper sponsored by parents. A spokesperson from each class should give a short "thank you" talk expressing the class's gratitude. Included in these talks should be ideas on how the students plan to use their education in the future.

Chapter III

The Ideal Family

Shalanda's family was temporarily held together by her faith-filled grandmother. Once grandmother took sick and died, the family as it had been soon disintegrated. When Shalanda's family life changed, with many friends offering support, she was able to sustain her attempts at self-improvement.

Families under God are blessed. Consisting of a father, mother, and children, they recognize the life they share is not their own to do with as they wish, but is shared by their Creator. Recognizing this gives them a sense of responsibility. They understand they're stewards of this life and must respect it as belonging to God. The ideal family has as its motto: In God We Trust. Members know and believe the love uniting them comes from God and is everlasting.

Family Prayer Time

Twice a day the ideal family gathers to praise and thank God for the blessing of life. Each family prays according to the beliefs and rituals of its own particular faith. What's important is to take time to pray as a family.

Meal Times

The ideal family gathers twice a day to share food and experiences. It's a special time to be filled with pleasant and respectful conversation. Table manners and respect for each other are observed. Grace is said before and after each meal. Occasionally, a meal might be shared with a new neighbor or one in special need.

Family Walks

Walks together as a family in the neighborhood or park are occasions for all to share what's new and exciting in nature, as well as provide opportunities for conversations with friends they meet along the way. The family should stroll slowly so the beauty of a butterfly or song of a bird won't be missed. This isn't the time to roller skate, ride bikes, or jog. The first priority is sharing with each other the glories of nature.

Church

The family should worship in whatever way its particular tradition of faith dictates. Church at a special time and place, however, is when God is acknowledged by a community of faith-filled families.

Parents and Grandparents as Volunteers

There are many ways parents, children, and grandparents can volunteer to help in their neighborhood, school, and Church.

Every person should contribute talent and time outside the family at least once a week.

Moral Virtues Taught

Moral virtues taught in school should be re-emphasized at home. Faith should be explained, taught, and practiced. Parents and grandparents should be good role models and examples of these virtues.

Family Chores Shared

Each member of the family should share in household chores. There's no payment for such duties. It's expected that all members of the family accept responsibility for doing their part to contribute to the household.

Family Gardens

Making family vegetable and flower gardens can be a wonderful time to share a common project, and is a tremendous learning experience. Learning how to care for tools, compost waste, feed birds, and care for garden seeds and plants, are but a few of the ways. Tools, as well as gardening tips, can be exchanged with neighbors. Harvesting and preparing vegetables can be special family times, also. Sharing and eating them together can be a real celebration of life.

The Family Pets

Pets in a family give children added responsibility. Learning how to care for and respect pets is a wonderful growing-up experience.

TV Limited

Family TV shows can be viewed and discussed together. Otherwise, TV should be limited to appropriate news and children's shows.

Toys

Children should not have toys suggesting violence or immoral behavior. Toys and bikes can be obtained from thrift stores or garage sales and repaired if needed.

No Dishwasher

Children should take turns doing dishes by hand with one parent. This is an excellent time for communication and learning on a one-to-one basis.

Clothes Hung Outdoors

Children can help hang clothes outdoors. They can experience the wonderful smell of fresh clothes.

Coupons

A good way to teach children how to save is to use coupons. They can watch for them and clip them as they appear in papers and magazines.

Food Share

For example, a family member can volunteer for two hours a month and qualify for $30 worth of fresh meats and vegetables for only $14.

Appreciation for Service

Services of mail, library, gas, electric, garbage, and newspaper workers should be acknowledged by the family. Children can write the thank-you notes.

Family Vacations

Families should plan vacations together. Every member should have a part in preparing for a vacation or assisting with return chores.

Creating Memories

Putting a 1,000 piece puzzle together as a family, for example, can develop patience as well as memory. It can then be preserved as a picture to be hung. Making a family quilt with cloth pieces from articles of favorite outgrown clothes can also become a family memory.

Bread and Pie Baking

Baking can create a smell and taste the family will remember. Making pastries together gives children an appreciation for the good things of the earth.

Chapter IV

The Ideal Church

Shalanda was given a very special gift: the gift of faith. Once she discovered a church in which she could share fellowship and express with others her thoughts of praise, petition, and thanksgiving, she felt renewed and enriched in her personal life. This, in turn, affected the way she cared for her family and helped her begin to be of service to others.

All members of a neighborhood family should belong to a neighborhood church by the very fact they live close by. There should be one basic creed based on love for all members. The word love in the Creed may have various meanings for people of different faiths, but the basic meaning of charity is the same for everyone.

The Creed

We believe in the greatness of every person, and that each has goodness and beauty to be shared for all eternity.

We believe the uniqueness of every person is a gift, and the precious mystery of life within each is to be understood only by the Creator.

We believe in the integrity of others, confident they'll try to follow the Light of Divine Grace as it's discovered by them.

We believe God's love is in our world, and the task before us is to show His love to all we meet.

We believe in the nobility of work as a creative expression of the best within us, and as our contribution to humankind.

We believe in the contagion of a smile, and that we have power to bring new life to others through our spirit of hope and cheerfulness.

We believe in the challenge of the future, fully realizing there can be no future unless it becomes alive in us through the present moment.

We believe suffering and persecution will be ours, since we have chosen to work for justice sake.

The Motto

The motto, *In God We Trust,* should be displayed on the church flagpole, as well as on a large banner in the front of the church.

Prayer Service

Services should be conducted weekly or more frequently by members of the church. Members should also be permitted to do homilies on different aspects of the Creed. People should pray together to God in praise, thanksgiving, sorrow, and petitions. The Lord's Prayer can be their common prayer.

Dress

Clean ordinary street clothes can be worn; no shorts or bare feet permitted.

Socials

After prayer each week, people should be invited to enjoy each other's friends. They should also invite new neighbors into their circle of friends.

Separate Socials

Socials for separate groups can be allowed if people not in the group are invited. Each Social should handle its own expenses.

Meditation Room

The church should have a Meditation Room open to the neighborhood at all times, day and night. This room can be carpeted and have a few cushioned folding chairs. Also, stained glass windows surrounding the room are desirable. The room must be a place of quiet at all times. People of all faiths must be welcome to use the Meditation Room. They can bring their own Bibles or reading materials from home.

The Ten Commandments

The ethics code taught and followed must be the Ten Commandments God gave Moses on Mount Sinai. Respect and responsibility should be stressed, as well as other moral virtues of honesty and faithfulness.

Finances

All bills for expenses should be presented to members, and each should contribute according to his or her ability. Believing in the Lord's blessing, members can each present their needs, and the Lord in turn will provide. Prayers of thanksgiving and praise should be said in response.

Transportation

The ideal church is a centrally located church building, enabling most of the neighborhood to walk to services. Those who can't should get rides from those with cars.

Collections of Goods and Clothes

These should be made only when there's a need. Goods should be personally delivered. Those in crisis usually have no way of transporting them.

Time and Talent

The church should be prepared to offer services to those in crisis, such as those affected by floods, fires, and tornadoes.

Appreciation Potlucks

Pot Luck Suppers can be held for police, firefighters, and teachers to show appreciation for all they do for the neighborhood.

Church Choir

Church choirs should share their expertise and talents with other churches. They might also sing for other churches, especially in the suburbs.

PART III

Chapter I

The Sponsor Program

Shalanda's resurrection came about as a result of people helping people. Some people lived far away in suburbia, but saw the need for involvement in the inner city. Through personal sharing of themselves and their talents, wonderful relationships developed. It's just such bridge-building efforts The Sponsor Program is intended to provide.

The Sponsor Program

Building bridges between people has always been an important goal of our mission work. Having lived in suburbia prior to living in the inner city, I was able to establish relationships in both areas. It was only natural that a bridge be built enabling people to share.

I began building bridges by inviting a family from suburbia to come to our inner city Mission House and share dinner with an inner city family. The inner city family came early to help me prepare the table, salad, and dessert, while the suburban family brought the hot dish. We used our best tablecloths and dishes. A beautiful centerpiece decorated the table. All were dressed in their Sunday clothes. It was truly a special and festive occasion.

Before the meal, it was important to take time to get acquainted. We sat and visited in the living room before each family came to the table. After everyone was seated, I said a blessing prayer and conversation was resumed. When the meal was over, names, addresses, and phone numbers were exchanged.

After the initial dinner evening, families were invited to meet again in whatever way and as often as they chose. Some families met for sporting events, some for backyard get-togethers, some for breakfast buffets, still others for field trip excursions or a concert. Those families who met often formed deep and lasting relationships. Wonderful friendships have developed over the twenty-year period. What beautiful and treasured memories to enrich their lives!

Chapter II

The Cookie Cart

If Shalanda's brother, Tony, would have become involved at The Cookie Cart, his untimely and violent death might have been avoided. He'd have found a secure place with mentors and scholarships to give him an opportunity to rise above the evil influences causing his death.

The Cookie Cart

Many inner city kids I came to know and love were killed as a result of gang violence. I taught these kids the Ten Commandments and to respect their neighbors, and their consciences wouldn't let them kill or steal. As a consequence, where they left gangs they were eventually hunted down and shot. During the wake for the twelfth young victim, I resolved to do something to keep kids out of gangs.

Since baking cookies was already a favored project, it seemed that giving children a dream of having their own store was a likely possibility. What enthusiasm they had as they started out to meet their goal of raising $5,000! A friend made a cookie cart with big wagon wheels and painted it bright blue. Children pushed the cart down to the church and parked it on church property, since we couldn't afford a license to leave it in public places. There they sold out their inventory every day, except Sunday, which is their day off. Soon their $5,000 goal was met and the children eagerly awaited having their own store.

With the help of many wonderful volunteers, an old building was renovated. A generous friend who owned his own baking business, donated most of the equipment. With the permission of several city officials, bakers were ready to bake and sellers were ready to sell. Their store was officially opened in 1989.

More volunteers, young and old, came to assist children with their ambitious project. It wasn't long before suburban churches began ordering our cookies for their socials. Orders grew, as well as the enthusiasm of the children.

Then a generous and faith-filled married couple named Tom and Audrey retired early, and after much prayer, decided to sell their home and possessions to come live and work with the people of the inner city. When they discovered The Cookie Cart, they knew it was where they'd concentrate their efforts.

Children receive stipends according to their degree of responsibility. Sellers receive $1.00 for every four $1.00 bags they sell. Also, children learn the art of saving. Any profits from cookie sales go into a scholarship fund for private education. It's hoped that through personal attention received at smaller schools, these students will be better able to pursue their dreams and careers.

The Cookie Cart is more than a business. It's where children find stable care and concern so often missing in their lives. They find a special friendship with Tom and Audrey, who they know have given their all to be there for them. The Cookie Cart children witness generous giving by many other volunteers who come to share their talents.

The experiences of sharing and cooperation, together with a large dose of ingenuity and imagination, are helping to change not just the face of the neighborhood, but also the hearts and hopes of those who live there.

The billboard which reads, "Help Kids Help Themselves!" sums up what The Cookie Cart is all about.